DISCIPLINED ATTENTION

How to Improve
Your Visual Attention
When You Drive

Kenneth C. Mills, Ph.D.

Profile Press

Disciplined Attention:
How to Improve Your Visual Attention When You Drive

Kenneth C. Mills, Ph.D.

Profile Press
111 Cloister Court, Suite 212
Chapel Hill, NC 27514

Library of Congress Control Number: 2005900135

Publisher's Cataloging-In-Publication Data
(Prepared by The Donohue Group, Inc.)

Mills, Kenneth C.
  Disciplined attention : how to improve your visual attention when you drive / Kenneth C. Mills.

   p. : ill. ; cm.
  Includes bibliographical references and index.
  ISBN: 0-942267-29-X

1. Automobile drivers--Psychology. 2. Motor vehicle driving--Psychological aspects. 3. Vision. 4. Attention. I. Title.

TL152.7 .M55 2005
629.283

Edited by Mary Hubley
Bluefish Bay Editing and Publishing Services
www.bluefishbay.com

First Edition
Printed in the United States of America
10 9 8 7 6 5 4 3

<u>Dedication</u>

To Julia,

May you have expanded vision throughout
your lifetime.

*"The real voyage of discovery consists
not in seeking new landscapes but in
having new eyes." --- Marcel Proust.*

Acknowledgments

Any writer who attempts to understand and comment on driving quickly learns that it is one of the most complex subjects imaginable, and that's just when the driver is navigating his or her own neighborhood. It is difficult to take into account each and every situation that confronts most of us on the road. Writing about driving, by necessity, involves the slow process of simplification and refinement. That requires friends and colleagues who are willing to read and give feedback about whether it all makes sense (and whether it doesn't). I am indebted to all of the following for enduring long and complicated drafts of *Disciplined Attention.*

The individual who started me thinking, and who was a constant source of encouragement during the entire process, was Keith Code. His intuitive knowledge of the visual processes involved in riding (and driving) are unparalleled. He simply gets it. He and his instructors also endured my wobbly riding through I don't know how many Level IV sessions of the California Superbike School. I've bugged Keith for more suggestions than I have a right to.

I also tested the limits of friends and colleagues with endless conversations about abstractions; how many dinner conversations can one have about allocating your attention before everyone's attention drifts? Peter and Kathy Kaufman, top instructors for the Motorcycle Safety Foundation, patiently listened to my vague conceptualizations, filling in the gaps with practical examples. Likewise, Scott Geisler offered insights about how to streamline the material to the average driver.

I am indebted to Rob Hubal, Doug Antonelli, and Joseph Drazkowski for enduring several painful revisions. Their scientific knowledge allowed me to stretch my thinking beyond the technical. They were able to rein me in when my speculations jumped too far from the science at hand. Jane Stutts of the Highway Safety Research

Center at UNC Chapel Hill provided illuminating research on distractions and, as important, careful editing about more precise language for translating the research into practical terms.

Law enforcement drivers are the best teachers. I thank Doug Pendergraft, William Fletcher Clay, Allen Smith, Raymond Isley, Barry Kreider, David Broom, and Russell Sheppard of the North Carolina Highway Patrol. I also am indebted to Paul Schaffer and George Allison of the Federal Law Enforcement Training Center (FLETC). A special thanks to Randy S. Jacoby, Coordinator, Precision Driving Training Center at Oklahoma State University.

I am forever grateful to Jon Sands of Roush Racing, Jeff Payne of Driver's Edge, and Dan Dineson and Mike McGovern of the Bondurant School of High Performance Driving. My conversations with Danny McKeever of Fast Lane and his son Dan McKeever of ALEM International provided invaluable suggestions throughout the manuscript, again translating the vague into the concrete.

I also offer special thanks to Scott Bogue, editor and friend, who patiently helped me pare down drafts that were too wordy or technical. His clear thinking brought home many of the points that were obscure.

Special thanks go to Barry Phillips and Brent Ward for support that goes well beyond friendship. I would also like to thank Leslie Collins, Suzanne Adkins, and Kathy Walker for their patient administrative support.

Finally, no project would be possible without enduring support and encouragement from a family that never lost faith in the writer. Thank you Marcia, Devon, Kathy and Julia Mills.

Warning and Disclaimer Statement

The techniques contained in this book are intended for instructional purposes only. The author and publisher accept no responsibility for any accidents or crashes resulting in bodily harm or property damage that might occur from doing the exercises or changes in driver ability that may be gained by the use of this material. The author and publisher do not guarantee that drivers will attain a higher degree of skills that others have by applying these techniques. Supplemental notes and endorsements from noted driving instructors that have used these techniques should not be taken as any guarantee as to the safety or competency that might be gained, but merely as personal experiences. If expert assistance is required, the services of a driving instructor or licensed driving school should be sought. Always observe local and state laws.

The suggestions offered in this book were derived from basic research and further review by driving instructors. They have not received wide-scale validation and field testing. They have not been evaluated in driver education courses or with formal studies. The reader's failure to follow the following warnings may be dangerous and cause them to crash or hit someone else. *Please use at your own risk.*

The suggested exercises in Chapter 6 are designed so that you will move your eyes to all parts of the traffic scene and gather more information. **It is important that you first do these exercises as a passenger in the front seat of the vehicle.** It is also important that when you drive, you practice these exercises under safe, non-congested traffic conditions, such as in an uncrowded parking lot.

See disclaimers in the beginning of Chapter 6 for further warnings.

Table of Contents

Chapter 1:
The Problem with Inattentiveness

How do we negotiate chaotic traffic? What determines whether we safely arrive at our destination or become involved in a collision? It all comes down to what we see, and how our brains manage that information. Professional drivers understand this. They know that their vision is key to driving an ambulance, a police car, or a racing car. Teenage drivers are not always as aware as professionals; when they make left turns across two lanes of traffic, for instance, their eyes often have difficulty scanning the scene and sorting out the innumerable stimuli— pedestrians, bicycles, and safe paths of travel. Like the professionals have learned, however, there are ways we can manage our visual attention and improve our driving.

The reality is that our eyes—and our visual attention—are our most important crash guards. The automobile industry would like us to believe, though, that drivers rely on steel, airbags, and automotive technology to protect them. However, most people believe they are skilled drivers and that *their skill* keeps them out of trouble.[1] A majority of drivers believe that inattention is the primary cause of crashes, more so than breaking laws or the lack of driving skills. And most drivers are willing to take conscious control of their attention to increase safety.

This book, *Disciplined Attention,* suggests ways to improve our attention on the road. The suggestions are derived from two groups of professionals: scientists who use simulations and video technology, and driving instructors who train the very best—law enforcement officers, corporate executive protection drivers, and emergency service drivers.

What do professional drivers know that the rest of us don't? They have learned to discipline their attention through techniques that eliminate dangerous habits such as target fixation, tunnel vision, and narrowed attention. This practical knowledge has passed informally from instructor to instructor, and then from instructor to student.

Science adds to our knowledge. In the last decade with the advent of computer "eye tracking" technology, scientists have gained an unprecedented insight as to how visual attention works and how distractions, stress, and a range of other factors affect both what we see and how we react to what we see. Scientists have discovered how we process traffic information, details that are not immediately obvious through casual observation. This new scientific knowledge is only beginning to be applied to driver education and training. The research provides a fresh and elegantly simple way to think about how we manage and use our attention to survive in traffic. It points to basic techniques that we might otherwise overlook. But the pure science has limits—it is often too abstract to be useful to the majority of people.

That's where this book helps; it offers clear examples and applications to explain the complex scientific data.

We have also engaged driving professionals, top instructors, who reviewed the material in *Disciplined Attention* and filled in many of the details. They helped develop the exercises in Chapter 6 to assist average drivers. This book provides exercises and techniques, once reserved for the professional in training, that you need to control your attention.

Driving presents challenges that we don't encounter in other life activities: challenges to our visual attention. Some drivers accept these challenges with enthusiasm. They find that honing visual attention can lead to altered states and a feeling of "flow."[2] They become driving enthusiasts. Other drivers are unaware and don't give visual attention a second thought. Between these two extremes are average drivers who know that attention skills are important, but who don't quite know how these skills develop. One goal of this book is to let drivers of all skill levels take on new challenges and develop new skills. Some of these skills may save your life.

Disciplined Attention does not teach how to maneuver, brake, park, or refine the motor skills that are essential to good driving. For novice drivers, those skills are best learned under the close supervision of an instructor or parent.[3] *Disciplined Attention* does not replace hands-on driving experience. As we discuss, all drivers can benefit from closed course driver training. Proficient drivers combine disciplined attention with knowing their personal limits and their vehicles' limits—a combination that is necessary to avoid a crash. Those limits can only be tested through long hours of practice on the road.

Disciplined Attention demonstrates how to put visual attention into practice. As a result, our new skills promise to increase safety—for ourselves and for those around us. They will also increase our confidence on the road. *Disciplined Attention* can even make driving more enjoyable.

The Need for Disciplined Attention

This book is directed to those readers who want to become safer, more confident drivers. It's for those who believe that there is more to driving than understanding stop and go and knowing how to steer. It explains one of the professional driver's most powerful tools, how it works, and how it can create a better driver.

Novice drivers can benefit by learning good attention habits before poor attention habits are acquired. If you are the parent of a teen who is about to start driving, there are practical techniques presented in *Disciplined Attention* that can be the basis for more advanced skills. Parents and teens will be able to immediately use *and share* the practical exercises in Chapter 6.

Individuals who are about to become professional drivers—cadets in law enforcement, firefighters, ambulance and truck drivers—can all benefit from reading *Disciplined Attention*. These professionals may receive excellent hands-on instruction in their training program, but they may also wish to have an understanding of the principles behind their training and to extend their formal training with exercises they can practice every day on the road.

In Chapters 1 through 5, *Disciplined Attention* gives an overview of the dynamics of visual attention and how it can go awry while driving. It describes how the eyes and brain work together to process visual information and explores research on hazard perception, target fixation, and the nature of distractions.

In Chapter 6, there are 10 practical suggestions for improving visual attention skills using simple techniques that can be practiced any time you are a passenger in the front seat. It takes just minutes a day to develop automatic routines that will allow you to take in visual information, separate what's important from what's not, and make clearer decisions in the face of complex, rapidly developing situations.

Cutting-Edge Research
Scientific Investigation into
Narrowed Attention

This book had its start over 20 years ago, when I began working with teams of scientists who were developing computerized tests to measure how people divide their attention among the many elements of a visual scene. This work was based on the belief that there are times, especially when there is a threat of some kind, when we cannot process all of the visual information bombarding us. During these times, our attention often becomes focused on a small portion of the scene while other equally important elements are ignored. This is commonly called *tunnel vision* (more precisely *attention narrowing*) and it plays a very important role in how we navigate complex traffic scenes.

Cognitive psychologists and neuroscientists have long observed the tunnel vision phenomenon in different guises. Studies over the last 100 years have demonstrated that our visual field narrows when adrenaline flows and we focus on a relevant threat.[4] [5] However, new studies suggest that our attention does not simply narrow, but that the brain also limits how we process the information in terms of space and time dimensions. These new studies start to explain what causes our thinking to shut down in times of crisis. They also point to training techniques aimed at overcoming that primitive natural reaction when it leads to danger on the highway.

The study of narrowed attention in older drivers is among the most exciting and rigorous science to emerge in the last 20 years. Karlene Ball and her colleagues at the University of Alabama at Birmingham mapped out how attention narrows in the "at risk" older driver. They precisely validated a test for drivers that measures the Useful Field of View (UFOV)®. The test documents the amount of visual information that a driver gathers in a brief glance without head or eye movements. As we will discuss in Chapter 5, the UFOV is the best predictor of accidents in older drivers.[6] Just as important, older drivers who receive training in expanding their UFOV have fewer accidents.[7]

Training is the way that we prevent our attention from tunneling or narrowing. We are discovering that attention-allocation skills follow the laws of learning. That is, they improve with practice, the task of learning can be broken down into manageable components, and feedback can be structured for each new skill. While this may seem like common sense, most drivers do not recognize that their attention skills can improve over a lifetime.

Experience of Driver Training Professionals

As I became more aware of how scientists investigate restrictions to our field of vision, I was also gaining exposure to professional trainers who teach vision and attention skills as the core of driver training courses. I brought professional driving instructors together into focus groups, where they explained what goes on as a driver learns to perform under a variety of stressful conditions. On the track, tunnel vision disrupts the essential skills associated with smooth, accomplished performance in cornering, braking, and evasive maneuvers. The instructors said that narrowed vision and disrupted attention are the greatest impediments to good driving. They said that the restriction of our visual field is demonstrated in a number of ways, as drivers navigate a variety of traffic challenges.

Expanding visual attention is a primary goal in courses that provide live driving experiences to police, firefighters, EMTs, professionals, corporate protective services, and teen drivers. According to Mike McGovern, the chief instructor at the Bondurant School of High Performance

Driving, learning to drive well starts with learning to pay attention to everything that is going on. During practice with skids, collision avoidance, and negotiating an intersection, the primary objective is to perform basic skills to expand vision and reduce disorientation under pressure.

Similarly, Jeff Payne, motorsports professional and founder of Driver's Edge, speaks enthusiastically of how teenage drivers largely overcome their narrowed attention after just a short exposure to live track training. Paul Schaffer and his colleagues from the Federal Law Enforcement Training Center (FLETC) in Glynco, Georgia, train between 35,000 and 50,000 law enforcement personnel a year (4,000–5,000 in driver training). FLETC colleagues spend much of their training resources on "live" exercises that train officers to keep their cool, not narrow their attention, and stay calm in life-threatening crises.

The Mechanics of Being Out of Control

Learning to control your attention is the basis for being in control during an emergency.

A moment, a split second, is the difference between being in control and being out of control. The difference is between merging safely and sideswiping another car, between making the corner and running off the road, between making a successful turn and having a head-on collision. For some people, such a moment happens infrequently, while for others it is a part of everyday survival. We are discovering that what it takes to stay in control is a skill that can be learned. Drivers who are in control learn how precious a split second is. Drivers (and athletes) who are about to lose control first lose control of their vision and attention.

As everyday traffic becomes more demanding, with more vehicles and roads designed for higher speeds, learning to control our visual attention is no longer something only professional drivers should learn to do. Training of visual and thinking skills that were once reserved for the professional are equally valuable to the new driver, to the mom who must manage children in the back seat while merging onto the freeway, and to the older driver whose skills haven't kept pace with the high speeds and heavy traffic so common today.

According to the AAA Foundation for Traffic Safety, driver inattention is a factor in more than one million crashes annually in North America alone, resulting in serious injuries, deaths, and an economic impact that some experts say reaches $40 billion per year.[8]

Is it necessary—or even possible—to practice our visual and attention skills when we drive? Don't these skills develop automatically? What can we learn from professional drivers to reduce our chances of a collision as we travel for business, run errands, or commute to school or work? To answer these questions, we'll begin by exploring how our visual attention skills are uniquely challenged when we drive.

Eye Movements

Our attention while driving is guided, millisecond-by-millisecond, by our eye movements. Learning to drive well is learning to discipline our eye movements.

As drivers, we lead with our eyes. Professional instructors repeat the mantra that "the eyes are the most important tools of the driver." Studies show that most of the time we focus our attention on where we look and that our actions and hand movements are closely linked to our eye movements.[9] This has a huge effect on how we drive ... *we go where we look.*

Conscious attention to planned eye movements appears to be a key factor in learning to perform safely and proficiently on the road. The more we practice precise eye movement patterns, the better the odds are that we will consciously see what is important and ignore what isn't. We will become more effective in identifying and dealing with hazards.

Visual Routines

The eyes lead by using visual routines—efficient, very brief mechanisms that allow us to organize the scene and let us deal with an incredible barrage of visual information that we encounter in all our activities.[10] [11] If it weren't for routines, we would simply be overwhelmed by the amount of data that would accumulate in the visual brain. Even driving a mile to the convenience store would soon be overwhelming because we would not have the memory capacity to store all the images. Routines allow us to organize the space and time dimensions of our world, from buttering our bread to taking a corner at 35 mph. We don't really store the exact nature of each and every scene that we encounter in our memory; rather, our brains store a memory of how we process scenes and moves. The memory of the process is the visual routine, the basic building block of performance.

Scientists think that we store routines as modules that allow us to perform similar tasks such as picking up a toothbrush or coins or a coffee cup. Another kind of routine we might store would be walking down the hall, negotiating a stairway, and going through a door. The exact timing and nature of the routine varies with the nature of the task. If you have a conversation with someone, it calls up different visual routines than sorting cards, catching a ball, or reading a poster. You will likely use different routines to make a left turn through congested traffic and to follow another vehicle.

A special type of routine, especially valuable to the driver, is "the sprite."[12] The sprite represents a set of attention-based routines that detect patterns of motion, filling in predictable details over time in the face of noise or absent images such as the motion of wheel or vehicle, the jump of fish out of water, or the way a ball bounces when dropped.

In driving and even in sports, both dynamic and attention demanding activities, a visual routine is the most efficient eye movement pattern that will gather information about the scene while at the same time guiding smooth and efficient motor movements. Routines depend on sequences of eye fixations: those momentary glimpses of visual objects that allow us to spot and recognize events. In many instances, our recognition of events is well below conscious levels, and working the background (pre-attentive). This means that visual routines are more often than not automatic.

Eye fixations in routines last from about 1/10th second to 3 seconds, averaging about 250 to 350 milliseconds for many common motor tasks. The fix duration varies by the task and from person to person.

Research with eye movements suggests that very few fixations are wasted. Our eyes lead. When we engage in simple sequential tasks such as those involved in driving, the eyes closely monitor every step of the process. The step-by-step tasks, or anchors, are often referred to as "reference points."

The current thinking is that routines are task or goal directed. They add an element of predictability to our visual world. We don't have to relearn our motor patterns each and every time we encounter a slightly different situation. There are re-usable routines that allow us to make a left or right turn, adjust the radio volume, signal, or use the rear view mirror without a lot of thought.

Routines are not just stimulus-driven, or as we discuss in Chapter 3, not just "bottom up" processing. They require memory storage and are "top down" driven. The short memory for visual routines is iconic, a stimulus representation that remains in the visual system after objects disappear from the retina, but rapidly fade when they are not present.

Routines lead a person's actions by just milliseconds most of the time. If you pick up a cup of coffee, your eyes precede your hand movements by fractions of a second. Your eyes will steal a momentary glance at the coffee cup, recognize it and its position, and you may even have a sprite that guides your hand. In the initial stages of learning, eye movements are more closely linked to actions.

It appears that when drivers learn, visual routines are acquired one step at a time. Drivers must first learn to take a corner slowly and become accustomed to the visual references before speed (and information processing) increases. Similarly, as a new driver learns to change lanes on the freeway, he or she will turn his or her head and use the mirror to gauge the gap and the speed of other vehicles. Basic perceptual skills must be acquired before advanced skills develop. Visual routines for an activity seem to grow more efficiently during practice that takes place in relatively uncluttered visual environments such as parking lots, less-congested traffic, simulators, and training courses.

Scientists don't know yet how routines fully develop in complex, disordered tasks such as driving, but it appears that as we make minor adjustments such as steering, our eyes gather millisecond-by-millisecond updates and we make corrections accordingly. These adjustments depend on behavioral goals, that is, our top down processes direct them. If the goal at a stop sign is to "stop and go," the visual adjustments (and consequences) can be drastically different from "stop, look left-right-left, then go."

You Go Where You Look

Michael Land and his colleagues at the University of Sussex in the U.K. show that "you go where you look" has scientific basis.[13] They examined the eye movements of drivers in a Jaguar taking corners along Queen's Drive round Arthur's Seat in Edinburgh, Scotland.[14] They found that in a curve, drivers spend much of their time fixating on the edge of the road near a point at the tangent (middle) of the curve, where the inside of the corner changes direction *(see Figure 1)*. The driver's eyes seek out this point one to three seconds before entering the corner and return to it from time to time throughout the corner. Half a second after entering a corner, a driver spends about 80% of their time fixating within 3° of the tangent point.

In a simulation study, the investigators selectively blocked out parts of the curves and examined performance. They found that when a driver enters a curve, an optimum look-ahead time of about 7/10ths of a second provided the best steering performance, regardless of speed.[15] However, when only parts of the road were visible, there were problems. When only the far part of the simulated road was visible, drivers matched the curve well, but they had difficulty staying in their lane. When only the near part of the corner was visible, steering was unstable and jerky. In the British authors' words, when the drivers could not see the whole corner, their steering went "from smooth to 'bang-bang.'"

Hands Move with the Eyes

According to George Allison with the Federal Law Enforcement Training Center (FLETC), the further ahead we focus, the smoother we steer...*and* place less lateral forces on the vehicle. In the flick of a second, *smooth* translates from the eyes to the hands to steering to vehicle dynamics.

Figure 1. *A half second after entering a curve, a driver spends 80% of the time looking within a small area (circle) of the tangent point where the inside edge of the bend changes direction. (Turn 15—The Roller Coaster, Virginia International Raceway, North Course.)*

But smooth doesn't develop overnight. Many driving instructors observe that hand movements are directly tied to eye movements, especially in the early stages of learning to drive. On the road or track, the hands of the beginning driver will move with each and every glance. If the student takes nine glances while going into a curve, the instructor observes nine hand movements. If the number of glances reduces to five, so do the hand movements. Hand movements translate into steering adjustments.

In track training, *smooth* evolves when the skilled driver is able to push his or her visual attention ahead in the scene and ignore the small stuff. But does that mean that the professional who drives in traffic only glances at the road far ahead? No. New research suggests that the proficient driver is able to gather visual information with brief glances to all parts of the scene, decide what is relevant and what is not, and move on. While looking ahead is frequently used on the track to establish "focus," it is less useful in day-to-day traffic because of all the peripheral things happening such as cross traffic, pedestrians, merges, and congested lane changes. However, good drivers in both track and traffic settings have the ability to use brief informative glances without locking onto a particular target.

Bruce Cabral with the Georgia Public Safety Training Center/A.L.E.R.T. International[16] offers a vivid example with police training that "you go where you look." In skid control training, some new drivers will not turn into the skids. The students are confused about which way the vehicle is skidding and when told to turn the steering wheel in the direction that the car's rear end is going, they become more confused. So Bruce and his colleagues installed a speed limit sign at both ends of the skid pan (a large surface covered with water) and told the students who were confused to forget the rear of the vehicle and just focus on the speed limit sign. The students were told, "Keep the front of the vehicle facing the sign and steer toward it. This is counter steering." It worked. Bruce's instructors also told the students not to use this system on the other driving exercises because they would hit an object on the course if they stared at it. The ones who didn't believe this got into trouble...they ran over cones, and when asked if they were staring they would say yes, they were not looking down the road.

The Eyes Stick

Unfortunately, the eyes stick. When they do, routines become stalled and the eyes don't move through reference points. Performance suffers and we loose smooth. From what we understand, one thing that causes our eyes to stick is target fixation.

Target fixation happens when the eyes momentarily lock onto a new unfamiliar event, sometimes a threat. We will explore the dynamics of target fixation and how to overcome it as a main theme in this book. Professional drivers learn how not to succumb to target fixation; they have helped to develop the exercises in Chapter 6 to prevent it.

The eye movements of the inexperienced driver (and some experienced drivers) are peppered with "target fixation" moments. In the most subtle form, target fixation is the tendency to lock onto opposing traffic, fixate on the squirrel darting into the road, or stare too long at the red cone in the parking lot course. The novice sees a potential threat and the glance lingers. Dan McKeever teaches that the driver's hands will also freeze when the eyes fixate too long.[17] According to McKeever, when the eyes lock up and don't gather new information, the hands don't know what to do.

Proficient drivers have learned *not* to move their hands when they execute an information gathering glance. As research in Chapter 5 suggests, experienced drivers do not stop moving their eyes to new targets; instead they look briefly up, down, left, and right to capture the whole scene. They have learned that to prevent target fixation, they must keep their eyes moving and their hands (and emotions) calm.

Driving Presents Unique Attention Challenges

The visual and attention skills for driving are unique, and are different from other everyday uses of attention. Driving requires continual divided attention to all parts of the visual scene.

The attention skills we need to stay safe on the highway are different from many other everyday attention skills. For instance, we don't have to stop and concentrate when we climb stairs, tie our shoes, or use kitchen utensils. However, driving presents special challenges: we have to continually divide our attention between more than one task at a time.

We have to simultaneously pay attention to lane position, the distance from the car ahead, brake lights, our instruments, and traffic conditions. And the multi-tasking requirements keep on coming, unlike other everyday experiences, at a pace often set by unpredictable traffic and rapidly unfolding events.

To make matters more complicated, threats on the highway approach quickly from all parts of our visual field, not just from a single source. A blowout from a truck tire in the inside lane can be coupled with a driver swerving from the center lane to the outside. The necessity to assess multiple threats presents a paradox to a visual and nervous system that evolved to handle dangers one at a time. *(More about that in Chapter 4.)* As a consequence, while driving, unexpected events can cause what some driving instructors refer to as "brain lock." It takes a moment (or two) while the driver sorts through all of the visual information, selects which hazards are important, decides how to manage the situation, and then takes action.

Emotional Arousal

How effectively you allocate your attention in traffic is influenced by your emotional state at the moment.

When we drive, we have to process complex, fast-paced scenes. We must continually assess risks, and at the same time, control our emotional reactions. How we allocate our attention depends not only on experience level, training, and conditions at the time, but also on our emotions and stress level.

Our emotions affect our capacity for attention to a much greater extent than we would expect. Our primitive survival reactions narrow our perceptions. They can quickly lead to a loss of control. Scattered, unfocused visual attention can become a permanent part of someone's driving style, but this style can also be overcome with specific training techniques.

When our emotions are really pumped, we can't perform well. For instance, when drivers first sign up for high performance driving on the track, they arrive in the morning tense and excited, ready to drive for the next eight hours. But new drivers become distracted in less than 20 minutes of high performance maneuvers! And drivers who become distracted are also more likely to make mistakes. New teen drivers who are distracted by their passengers are much more likely to crash.[18]

Disrupted Attention

Disrupted attention is defined by a mild disorientation and a decrease in the driver's ability to process information from all parts of the visual scene. Becoming aware of how attention is disrupted may only seem important to professional drivers who routinely face danger, but new drivers, experienced drivers, and older drivers can all benefit.

The Impaired Driver

Think of driver performance as being on a continuum, kind of like a vertical ruler, with the measurements ranging from very bad to very good. At the very top of the continuum is the accomplished law enforcement instructor. He or she can handle complex decisions; this person has practiced so much that reactions are automatic and simple. Emergency maneuvers are accomplished flawlessly, even when they're coming at lightning speed.

At the very bottom of the continuum is the impaired driver. He or she may be using illegal drugs or experiencing adverse effects from prescription drugs. Of course, the drunk driver anchors this end of the continuum. He or she cannot handle the demands of complex decisions. At a blood alcohol level of .08 percent, the legal limit in the U.S., attending to one-dimensional tasks such as following the double yellow line may seem possible to them. Drunk drivers often try to assure themselves that if they drive carefully and stay to the right of the centerline, they will make it home safely. Then, at that fateful intersection, curve, or merge in which attention is required for more than one task, alcohol-impaired drivers' eyes and brains cannot cope with the additional demand.

Alcohol impairs nearly every aspect of a driver's information processing abilities.[19] The brain's control of eye movements is highly affected by alcohol. When driving, a person's eyes must focus briefly on important events and track them along with the vehicle's motion. Low to moderate levels of alcohol disrupts voluntary eye movements. It increases the time it takes the driver to read a sign or respond to a signal, and impairs his or her ability to track moving targets.[20]

A lesser-known fact is that the impaired driver also experiences tunnel vision.[21] When the blood alcohol level reaches only half the legal limit, the visual field starts to narrow. At .08 percent, visual deterioration is well underway. The ultrafine muscles that coordinate eye movements are unable to simultaneously grab elements of the visual field from the periphery and the focal point.

The continuum is anchored at the bottom by extreme tunneling and impairment. At the top are the drivers who can repeatedly gather information from all parts of the scene, even in the face of escalating demands. Their routines don't stick and they seldom tunnel.

Distractions

Distractions increase the potential for disrupted attention.

During day-to-day driving, hours of boredom are interspersed with moments of terror. Most of us, most of the time, do not experience challenges to our attention. With no apparent hazards close by, we often see little risk in distracting ourselves with cell phones, food, makeup, passengers in the back seat, newspapers, radios, or navigation systems. We may have a sense that there are times when we should avoid distractions, such as using the cell phone during high-speed congestion. The problem is, most of us do not know when it is and when it is not appropriate to engage in distracting activities. We generally believe that if an emergency arises, our attention skills will kick in; and while we will be pushed to their upper limit, we feel that we would be able to handle the emergency. We may justify engaging in distractions by believing it is too difficult to stay focused and alert for long periods, and that emergency situations are rare.

Distractions have the power to interrupt routines. They divert thoughts while simultaneously disrupting the "wide view" that is necessary to effectively scan the road. Distractions compromise a driver's ability to detect motion, monitor changes in the driving scene, and track the split-second timing of traffic events. More critically, distractions compromise the ability to gather information from all parts of the visual field. There is evidence that the cognitive demands of a cell phone conversation, under some circumstances, can be as disruptive as driving at the legal blood alcohol level of .08.[22]

The Attention Attitude

Learning to allocate our attention more proficiently while driving is an attitude.

Becoming more aware of how we allocate our attention when we drive is as much attitude as it is skill, and it appears to be an attitude born from exposure to challenges.

Once a driver realizes how difficult it is to spot and react to a sudden hazard, and to keep control of the vehicle during a violent reaction, he or she usually becomes more careful. In the process, the driver gains a greater respect for the vehicle, but more importantly, a greater respect for his or her own limits as a driver.

On the track or in fast-paced simulations, teens who have not yet developed complex visual attention and decision-making skills express surprise when they cannot stay as calm and composed as older, more experienced drivers seem to be able to do. They are just starting to realize that being alert while driving is a full time activity. Experienced drivers usually perform better because they know that being alert gives them that millisecond advantage to plan and anticipate the unexpected. A select few have acquired the attitude that paying attention to their attention may be the most important skill of all.

A Lifetime of Learning

Improving visual attention skills is not limited to novice or elderly drivers. These skills can be developed over a lifetime.

Professional trainers believe that we can improve our attention skills year after year. However, most drivers do nothing to hone their skills during long hours in the car. Many drivers assume that their attention skills are adequately developed; they have become comfortable with their day-to-day driving challenges. This familiarity promotes a sense of immunity from accidents.[23] Some drivers don't recognize the value in attention training because they assume this training is intended only for professional drivers. Others simply don't believe that such an easily acquired skill can yield a large payoff. However, most professional driving instructors teach that we can improve our attention skills during our everyday driving routines. Drivers who are best at hazard perception are actively involved in viewing their traffic environment; they are engaged in and are focused on the task of driving.

Improving visual attention skills while driving can be a self-rewarding activity.

The evidence from driver training schools and laboratory research reinforces the simple truth that improving our visual attention skills reduces the likelihood of collisions. Improving the skill of visual attention results in mastery and the satisfaction that comes with it.

Chapter 2:
How People Drive:
The Learning Process

The art of driving is defined by
calm, smooth, fluid performance.

Watch NASCAR and Formula 1 drivers.
They drive smoothly. Without exception,
driving instructors will tell you that optimal
performance begins and advances with
smooth, controlled movements. In road and
track schools, with live, hands-on driving
experiences, well-developed visual and
cognitive skills are inseparably linked to
smooth performance.

Smooth, proficient driving depends on visual
attention that is free from distractions.

The art of smooth driving rests on
simplicity. The expert clears his or her mind of
all clutter, and focuses only on the road
ahead, the next corner, the next visual
challenge, the next steering and speed
adjustment. The mental "noise" is far in the
background.[24] [25] A skilled driver remains calm
and focused when an emergency unfolds,
choosing possible escape routes, executing
smooth evasive actions, and maintaining the
delicate balance between steering and
braking. Experts don't think about the million
details in their perceptual field or the

hundreds of possible actions. Rather, they are above it all, selecting only the few critical items on which to concentrate.

The science of driving studies the factors that disrupt smooth, proficient performance.

Most scientists are not concerned with how well we find a corner line, or accelerate through a turn, or brake without dramatically upsetting the suspension, but they are interested in the factors that cause crashes. They are intrigued with modest changes in attention that can alter how well we negotiate an intersection, or spot a pedestrian, or keep the car on the road.

Because it's so familiar, it is easy to underestimate how complex driving is. It's an activity that requires a constant flow of decisions, together with input from all of our senses. To drive only a mile to the convenience store, the driver requires 1) at least three kinds of memory storage; 2) intact visual perception; 3) focused and wide view mechanisms; 4) a sense of balance and motion (even in a car); and 5) the ability to formulate an executive plan or roadmap of where he or she is headed.

Most modern views of driving generally agree that we use our mental resources to process information at three levels when we drive:

- **The Strategic Level**: higher-order complex thought that includes general trip planning, route selection, and risk assessment. Strategic thinking allows the driver to remember all sixteen corners during a track session and how to get to work or school each day. Police observe that if a driver is lost and not sure if he or she is to take a turn at an intersection, the driver will automatically turn down the radio volume while reading a street sign. The noise from the radio is a distraction to the individual's ability to perform strategic processing.

- **The Tactical Level**: requires selective attention and conscious control by the driver. This is the area of rapid learning by the novice and includes vehicle maneuvering, gap and distance estimation, and hazard perception. This is likely the stage at which new techniques for visual learning can be introduced.

- **The Operational Level**: tracking of events, adjustments to steering, speed and braking. This level quickly becomes automatic, fast and relatively inflexible after conscious practice. Skills reach this level of processing with extended practice or experience. Disruption of scene processing is most likely done at this level if specific, well-practiced routines are not in place or are impeded. For example, marijuana is most likely to disrupt this level of driving performance.[26]

Learning to drive well can occur at different levels and at different times in a driver's life. An older driver may learn that trip planning decreases exposure to heavy traffic, lowers the number of hazards, and minimizes the demands on steering, turning, and braking.[27] A new motorcycle driver may gather tips on how to look for unique road surfaces that might upset traction. A teen driver may realize that the presence of other teens in the car influences the tendency to become distracted and the ability to judge the approaching speed of other vehicles.

As scientists have recently started to correctly identify the attention-allocating skills needed for driving, we are employing new techniques to improve driving. For example, in the past, scientists believed that perceptual skill learning was task-specific; in other words, that visual skills learned in one setting did not transfer to new settings. However, in recent studies, it has been found that skill transfer is the rule rather than the exception, even when transferred from playing video games to actual driving.[28] Driving professionals and enthusiasts are increasingly discovering that videotape or video game track experience is valuable before the actual experience. Yet these games barely scratch the surface of driver training. In Chapter 5, we explore how technology and science have come together to offer an exciting variety of tools to train drivers.

The Need for Training

To make learning manageable, training for complex tasks often uses "training wheels." Remember learning how to ride a bicycle? With the help of training wheels, we learned to navigate the sidewalk and get a feeling for balance. The trick for Mom or Dad was to guess when it was the right time to take off the training wheels. Too soon, and we might crash, get hurt, and avoid bike riding for a while longer. Too late, and we wouldn't move on to the more challenging skill of balancing on just two wheels, experiencing the joy of riding, and integrating all of the new skills into one complete whole.

When we first learn to drive a car, we similarly have "training wheels." For the most part, we start out in relatively safe environments such as the school parking lot, and move gradually to neighborhood streets, then to more challenging, faster sections of roadway. Once we have some experience, we become confident and take the training wheels off, and we (implicitly) believe that we are mentally prepared for emergencies. Certainly, if we have driven for years without an accident we have confidence that we have mastered all of the skills we need to deal with any traffic situation.

As a new driver becomes more familiar with the vehicle and with traffic, he or she "automates" many skills. This is often referred to as overlearning. True, during 99% of our day-to-day driving, our skills have reached the tactical or overlearned level and we function well on automatic. Our confidence is based on *seemingly* extensive experience at something we do every day. We know how to steer and how to brake, and most of us are proficient in the rules and regulations of driving. But we are deceiving ourselves. In the very familiar activities that we do every day, we have a tendency to minimize the probability of bad outcomes. Drivers develop a sense of immunity to crashes, based on their subjective assessment of their own driving skills and the fact that crashes are infrequent. As a result, overlearning is coupled with overconfidence. Police crashes, for instance, are more likely to occur after an officer has been on the job from three to five years.

Most people believe that:

1. I am a good driver.
2. I can handle emergencies.
3. Accidents happen to others.

Most drivers are not trained for the unexpected.

Our beliefs about our emergency reactions are in error; most drivers simply aren't prepared for the unexpected. With few exceptions, we aren't trained to calmly allocate our attention to **both** high priority events and the whole scene at the same time under pressure.

In short, if we don't know where to look when things start happening quickly, we won't know how to act. The research suggests that our "emergency" attention skills don't improve automatically, and in fact, can degrade if we don't consciously reinforce them. Top law enforcement instructors say that the lack of emergency attention skills has a direct relationship to the lack of emergency driving skills in most drivers.

Attention skills need continual practice.

With most complex behaviors, if you don't develop and practice specific skills, the skills won't be there when you need them.

Your attention-based skills are no exception. If you don't practice the visual and attention skills that might be associated with an emergency, they won't be available when the action heats up.

The airline industry is well aware that pilots will forget skills that they don't often practice. Pilots must attend refresher training courses every six months to be allowed to fly without "training wheels." These courses reinforce how to recover from emergencies that place demands on memory and decision making. To pass the course, pilots are forced to attend to all parts of a scene while under pressure: cockpit gauges, flight controls, runway, navigation, and input from other personnel. It is no wonder that pilots are among the professions that are least prone to automobile accidents.[29]

Because we use our driving skills daily, we assume they are well developed. We become complacent and increasingly add time sharing into our driving practices. However, the attention and visual skills required for an emergency are not overlearned, and in many cases are never learned in the first place. Most drivers take their training wheels off way too soon.

Chapter 3:
Controlling Attentiveness

Basics of Disciplined Attention

Disciplined Attention (*def*): Using visual techniques to achieve mastery over attention while performing complex and challenging activities.

Disciplined attention is a continual, long-term process to enhance visual attention skills through conscious exercises. Disciplined attention is thus a learning tool to help the driver allocate his or her attention in a way that increases the chances of survival on the highway.

Achieving disciplined attention is based on the following assumptions:

- **Safe driving.** Most drivers place a high premium on the safety of their passengers, as well as on their own safety. Most people think they are skilled drivers and they believe that their skill keeps them out of trouble. Professional drivers and researchers alike believe that improved driver skills prevent collisions.[30]

- **Training.** Training can improve fundamental perceptual/cognitive skills and thus can improve driving performance. Like any other complex activity, driving depends on the development of basic skills before advanced skills develop. In many instances, improving visual attention is *necessary* to improve driving skills.

- **Attitude.** How you allocate your attention is as much an attitude as it is a skill. In drivers who perceive a value in disciplining their attention while driving, actual skill development is fairly rapid and straightforward. Conversely, drivers with an aggressive or angry attitude are likely to get over their heads in traffic situations that they have created.

- **Accepting responsibility**. People often blame collisions, poor habits, and generally stupid behavior on others. Most people think the offending driver is the other guy, not themselves.[31] To improve attention, each driver must take responsibility for his or her development and driving habits.

- **Scene processing.** Efficient scene processing is necessary for proficient driving. Efficient scene processing allows a person to *predict* future events, sometimes just a fraction of a second before they occur.

- **Uncompromised skills.** Anything that disrupts timing and spatial attention can compromise driving skills—such as drugs, fatigue, distractions, worry, or stress. For example, distractions disrupt the ability *to predict* hazards.

- **Switching states of attention**. There are two states of attention that are critical to good driving: distributed (ambient) attention and focused (selective) attention. Proficient driving relies on the ability to readily switch between the two.

- **Detecting hazards.** Detecting and moving one's eyes to a road hazard is a fast and largely automatic reaction. It is influenced by how familiar the person is with the hazard. If his or her mind is elsewhere, the automatic threat warning system slows. The ability to detect and respond to a hazard depends largely on the specific experience that the person may have had with the hazard.

- **Checking emotions.** There is no perception without the influence of emotions. Calming the emotions improves perception in highly charged dynamic tasks. The influence of emotions on visual perception is a primitive process and occurs in all people. As emotional arousal increases, the ability to switch between the distributed and focused scene processing is reduced. Further, stress increases the emotional input and increases the odds that attention will become restricted when the stakes are high. This means that an angry or upset driver will have fewer perceptual resources available. However, practicing disciplined attention in stressful situations can lessen some of the effects of emotions in a real emergency.

- **Staying in control.** Loss of control in an emergency situation often happens when scene processing is disrupted and the ability to shift between attentional states is lost. Disorientation can occur in less than a second.

- **Expanding field of view.** Expanding the driver's field of view through training and conscious exercises is one of the more effective means to reduce collisions.

- **Clean visual routines.** Clean *visual routines*, or practiced eye movement patterns, deliver optimal driving performance. For example, using an established visual routine as a person makes a left turn across a busy intersection will increase the chances that he or she will accurately assess all the elements of risk in the scene. Clean visual routines are relatively noise-free eye movement patterns that are organized across both space and time. They precede smooth motor responses. They are refined with training and experience, particularly early experience.

"Zoom Zoom"
Control of a Driver's Attention

The "zoom" reaction is what happens to a driver's attention when a hazard appears. This reaction is automatic most of the time. For example, a driver's zoom reaction will switch on when he or she approaches a difficult, unfamiliar corner; his or her attention automatically focuses on the most immediate, quickly approaching, high priority event. This very primitive mechanism is the basis for how we learn to allocate our attention when we drive.

Zoom in attention for focus and detail.

For years, cognitive scientists have used the metaphor of a zoom lens to distinguish between focused and distributed attention. Proficient driving performance depends on two states of attention:

1. focused attention (the detail view)
2. distributed or ambient attention (the wide view)

For instance, we zoom in for better focus. Our attention is in close, picking up details essential for survival. The center of the eye is extremely sensitive, and its eight million or so receptors process tons of complex information. The eyes process details such as shape, color, texture, size, slant, edges, and any fine-grained characteristic that might provide information about a threat. We glance briefly at the instruments, road signs, the road surface, obstacles in the roadway, merge signals, and maybe the facial expression on the driver in the next lane...looking for information that is relevant.

Zoom out for wide-angle view
and potential new threats.

Zoom out for the wide-angle (or ambient) view. Our visual system is on alert for new potential dangers. The view is way down the road, scanning the side mirrors, and glancing to adjacent traffic.

Zoom in fast to a threat or hazard.

Zoom in starts a "fight or flight" reaction. An orienting response kicks in instantly when a new, perhaps threatening event enters our perceptual space. Primitive alerting systems activate ever so delicately. Adrenaline flows, oxygen is shuttled to limb muscles, our heart rate may increase slightly, our respiration gets shallower, our circulatory system sends blood to limb muscles, and we generally get ready for the threat. When we zoom in, our hands will stop guiding the vehicle; our hands don't have enough new information to perform the next move.

The fight or flight reaction is characterized by perceptual (what we see and hear) as well as motor (muscle movement) readiness. Modern neuroscience teaches that we respond to a threat in two ways: one conscious and rational, the other unconscious and innate.[32] [33] The conscious response might take a brain path that takes a few seconds, is routed through the frontal cortex, and integrates our long-term memory stores with real time sensory data. The unconscious response routes the sensory information through the threat warning system in our midbrain, which in turn sends an alarm to the brainstem within a fraction of a second. When the threat warning system activates, the primary motor response is to mobilize and the primary perceptual response is to freeze.

The visual equivalent of freezing is target fixation; we sustain our focus exclusively on one threat and direct all of our actions toward it. Target fixation is the extreme of the zoom reaction. It is an adaptive process that can cause accidents behind the wheel. The brainstem takes control of our perceptual functions and we are forced to use automatic fight-flight reactions to handle complex demands. While we can learn to use the conscious/rational system to discipline our attention in emergencies, it takes training. Once started, the zoom reaction runs its course unless there are well-established attention habits and motor memories to supplant it. As we discuss later, part of that learning involves consciously moving our eyes to the next potential threat.

The extent of the zoom reaction is proportional to the extent of the threat.

The zoom reaction is infinitely adjustable. Mild threats can induce a mild zoom reaction, while moderate threats induce a moderate reaction and so on. Before the advent of eye-movement research, it was generally assumed that target fixation or tunnel vision happened suddenly, only in response to extreme emergencies. But that does not seem to be the case. If we reacted to each and every hazard with extreme target fixation, we would never leave the driveway. Yet if we didn't react modestly to mild threats, they might, in fact, materialize into greater ones.

The zoom reaction is also fast; perhaps the fastest reaction in our entire biological matrix.[34] The whole process may activate in as little as 1/10th of a second and may be fully underway within a half a second.

In a crisis, these primitive emotions allow the driver to immediately shift to automatic processing. The complex cognitive resources (the strategic and tactical levels discussed in Chapter 2) that the driver uses to interface with the car, the roadway, and even the route are tossed aside to direct his or her attention to the immediate danger (the operational level discussed in Chapter 2). The typical complex thinking involved in planning is bypassed.

Let's "ride" through an example. We'll take a drive through a wooded backcountry road in the mountains of Tennessee. Our driver is a high school senior, and his dad is the passenger/coach. The driver has been through the drills in the school parking lot to ensure that he understands steering and sudden stops. This is his first drive on the open road. He's cruising along, unconsciously switching between focused and distributed scene processing. Road signs receive fleeting notice that last about 2/10ths of a second, but opposing traffic on the curve receives focused gazes that last up to several seconds.

The driver is gathering information from all parts of the perceptual landscape at the same time. He's aware at some level of the entire scene: the edge of the road, the tree line a quarter of a mile ahead, the lane position of the car, engine sounds, and even the scent of pine trees (the windows are open). There is modest time pressure on his attention system as he gathers information, makes minor decisions and adjustments, and moves on to the next task. The teen is making steering adjustments that take 700 milliseconds between spotting the next apex, turning his head, and turning into the corner. He's not particularly conscious of the time pressure, but he knows that his awareness is heightened more than if he were watching TV. The task at hand is sufficiently complex to demand perhaps 70 to 80 percent of the new driver's total attention. Some brain capacity remains to think about the upcoming history final.

As he exits from a right hand corner and readies for the next left hand turn, he notices a slight movement on the right. Nothing drastic, just a hint of something out of the ordinary. He's going the speed limit of about 55 miles per hour and closing on the new event at about 80 feet per second. At first the movement is just barely discernible from other objects that whiz past. He consciously takes his foot off the accelerator and starts to slow. As another two seconds pass, he sees a gray bumper and realizes that a logging truck is entering the road.

In that instant, his visual system locks onto the truck. Attention narrows to just the threat, and other perceptual systems shut down. The 20 to 30 percent of spare attention is gobbled up in an instant. The engine noise is quieter. Dad's voice fades to the background. Distributed (ambient) attention is all but blocked out. The target fixation is most likely happening not just in the eyes, but also in multiple "higher" brain systems at the same time. Time is distorted. Afterward, the driver may say that time slowed to a crawl and the red truck was the only event that he could recall about the entire stretch of roadway.

The new driver's heart rate may jump 10 or 15 beats per minute.[35] His forearms immediately become tense and he increases grip pressure on the steering wheel. There is also tension in his back and legs.

Most importantly, he experiences a moment of visual panic. His attention and eye movements shift from calm scene processing to rapid, scattered eye movements as his brain searches for more information about what is happening. The characteristic "goal directed" scene management that was taking place just a few seconds ago is replaced with somewhat frantic yet automatic reactions.

Setting up for the next corner is now difficult. When his attention locks onto the truck, he immediately loses the ability to scan the entire scene. The cues that make up the horizontal reference become blurry, and there can be an uncoupling of the visual and the vestibular (balance) systems. In extreme cases, the resulting vertigo can cause dizziness, loss of balance, blurred vision, and nausea.

The inexperienced driver's first reaction is to hit the brake when sensing trouble. Often this is the wrong reaction and will make the situation worse. In many instances, hitting the brakes will start a skid and a loss of vehicle control.

The new driver's decision making, which is a higher-order cognitive process, is also compromised. Because his goal-directed attention and eye movements that are essential to navigate dynamic environments are disrupted, the driver does not look ahead to the next corner. There is the potential for the driver to become disoriented. The result can be a sloppy or even dangerous turn through the next curve.

Emotions and perception are now linked. The mild emotional arousal forces the driver to respond efficiently to what happens next. His emotions are adaptive: the arousal restricts attention to what is important and tunes out what is not. The driver seeks visual references for an immediate escape route, and tunes out the less important plan of stopping soon for lunch.

If the driver is able to selectively pay attention to the truck *and* visual cues in all parts of the scene, then he has learned to control the zoom reaction.

If the driver has not had the experience or training to consciously relax when the zoom reaction hits, strong primitive emotions (and reactions such as hitting the brakes) can quickly become counterproductive.

If there are other sources of emotional tension that were already in play, such as the natural teenage conflict with Dad, or worries about grades, the zoom reaction can be pushed over a threshold from where it is difficult to return to a wide-angle view. When the driver's attention reaches overload, it will either deteriorate into frantic eye-movement searching for a way out or freeze and lock onto the threat. In the worst-case scenario, the high school driver will head his car directly toward the logging truck and crash.

The driver's ability to remain calm in the face of a surprise and to know what to do next is at least in part a function of how many similar challenges he has successfully faced in the past. This is true for novice and experienced driver alike. Learning not to hit the brakes immediately with each new emergency is born of experience. Learning not to tense up and take a death grip on the vehicle controls when a true hazard appears is an acquired skill. Learning to formulate a visual escape route is a learned behavior.

The driver who has not learned to stay calm and has not developed disciplined attention and visual habits to guide the next actions faces further potential problems. If the target fixation doesn't cause a crash immediately, the resulting increase in arousal and disorientation in the next few seconds can translate into a feeling of loss of control. The driver can become acutely aware of his symptoms of panic, and while few who have experienced this are able to verbalize the increase in random eye movements, many say they feel a pounding in their head, their vision becomes blurry, they sweat profusely, and they are unable to focus. The inability to make a decision is a common report. The feeling of loss of control can also take up semi-permanent residence as a conditioned fear response. Then, similar yet less threatening events such as cross traffic can trigger target fixation.

Thus, training to control the zoom reaction gives the driver control over the immediate situation *and* similar emergencies in the future.

The end of the story? Our new driver pulls it off. He remembers the evasive action swerve that was part of his closed course driver training. He looks at the truck, envisions an escape route, accelerates, swerves gently to the left as the truck starts to cross, swerves to the right, and passes safely. He has practiced life-saving attention control that allows him to remain calm in a crisis, preventing a minor incident from turning into a major one.

Memory Systems and Processes

Seeing is our most important sense on the road. It gives us highly reliable information about the locations and properties of environmental objects while they are still distant—and still not dangerous. For the driver, those objects are vehicles and traffic details that are closing in fast. Top driving instructors will tell you that good visual and attention habits are absolutely essential for good driving habits.

Bottom Up Versus Top Down Processes

The driver's visual system is the primary link to the immediate future.

A driver's visual perception uses both passively stimulated responses ("bottom up" processing) and an active model of the driving environment ("top down" processing) second by second to predict what will happen in the future. Bottom up processing is automatic and stimulus driven. It is our response to inherent qualities of visual stimuli such as brightness, movement, color, shape, size, and motion. This process is innately wired and our reactions are fast and automatic. On the other hand, top down processing is task-dependent and goal-directed. It is memory dependent, established by previous experiences and by immediate goals. Top down processes are learned associations we form. For example, a bottom up experience happens when we instantly attend to the movement of a pedestrian running toward the street, while a top down experience occurs when we notice a rest area sign that we have been anticipating.

Your working model for driving is based upon your visual memory.

Most of the visual memory that you need to predict your next moves is used and discarded in seconds.

Memory Systems

The top down model for driving engages three types of memory. Each memory function corresponds to the amount of time that the visual system holds the scene. The three memory functions are:

- **Iconic memory:** immediate scene capture

- **Short-term memory (STM)**: working memory and knowledge of the road environment

- **Long-term memory (LTM):** visual plans, traffic schemas, and cognitive maps

We need only a very limited amount of information from the environment to get from the current road position to the next. At any given moment, so much sensory information is bombarding us that our primary task is to shut much of the information out rather than attend to it. If we tried to retain all of the information presented to us, our memory demands would be overwhelming. Instead, we compensate by attending to only certain parts of the visual scene.

Iconic memory is a visual snapshot of the immediate road scene. Iconic memory is put into play when we glance at a scene for a second or two and gather information about where our vehicle will be in the immediate future in relation to where we are now. The visual processing for the eyes to acquire a new target takes just 200 to 300 milliseconds.

The actively processed visual information that we draw from iconic memory is then transferred into working, or *short-term memory (STM)*. Any visual information that is not actively processed is lost, replaced quickly by information from the next snapshot. By eliminating the unimportant information, our brains effectively reduce the memory demands required for driving.

Knowledge from *long-term memory (LTM)* such as memory of road signs and past history with traffic patterns is also transferred into working memory. Long-term memory is a learned reaction to visual cues such as stop signs and previously experienced traffic conditions. Like iconic memory, long-term memory also feeds the short-term memory; it provides STM with mental blueprints that help organize and retrieve the information it contains.

Long-term memory captures its schematic views of traffic scenes by actively processing what we currently have in our short-term store. That is, we are constantly revising how we see the world based on what we are currently seeing. Experience matters. The more experience with traffic patterns, road conditions, and times driven along a certain path, the better organized and broader our schematic knowledge will be. For example, a police officer's long-term memory should include a cognitive map of his "beat" such as the curve on Rock Creek Parkway between Beach and 7th Streets as a benchmark.

You have such maps, too. If you close your eyes now, you can likely remember the salient features of your commute to school or work. You may see the road and may even feel the movement of the car over the surface. That is part of your long-term memory of knowing how to drive.

In our short-term or working memory we assess what is going to be dynamically navigated in a few seconds. In this working memory, we compare our past traffic experiences with our immediate perception of the traffic scene. Information held in short term memory changes quickly, depending to some extent on immediate behavioral goals. For example, if our goal is to direct the car through "The Snake" at 5a, 6, and 6a (*Figure 2*), we process iconic and schematic long-term information in working memory to get through the curves, discard it, and begin to gather new information at turn 7 as we enter the corner (*Figure 3*). There, we must perform hard braking as we go uphill to the right to the top of the hill. Then working memory gets refreshed as turns 8 and 9 suddenly appear.

Figure 2. *Take a number of quick glances at this photo to see how much you can remember when you close your eyes. (Turn 5a, 6, 6a—The Snake at Virginia International Raceway, North Course.)*

Whether we are on the way to the grocery store or setting up for turn 7, our visual attention, and memory skills allow us *to predict* our next moves. They may even serve to predict the moves of other drivers. Stripes on racecars originated to identify the novices who might not be as predictable as the seasoned veterans. But we don't have that advantage in everyday traffic, so to drive safely we need to rely on disciplined attention to predict the moves of other drivers and to plan our own moves.

Figure 3. *Turn 7, hard right, uphill, blind entrance to turns 8 & 9 at Virginia International Raceway, North Course.*

Our driving skills depend on our three different memory functions. The information that gets into our memory depends on our learning. We can improve our driving with exercises that selectively enhance memory skills.

In Chapter 6, there are exercises on the two-second glance, expanding your field of view, and conscious switching. These exercises will enhance your information-gathering capabilities, and overcome some of the limits of your iconic memory. Exercises on target and motion relevance and narrative driving will improve how you process what is in your short-term memory. Finally, exercises on formulating a visual plan and anticipating the moves of other drivers will reinforce new ways to organize your thoughts about driving.

Visual Systems—
The Wide View and Detail View

Two states of attention are required for effective driving: distributed or ambient attention (the wide view), and focused attention (the detail view).

The wide or peripheral view is quick. Information processing is up to 25% faster for stimuli that are located at the side of the visual field than for stimuli at the center of the visual field.[36] This may seem like an insignificant detail, yet it supports the notion that an ultrafast processor picks up the initial signal of potential danger, and a slower (but still fast) processor distinguishes the precise nature of the threat.

The detail view is controlled by a small region at the center of the retina of the eye, called the fovea, which contains densely packed cones. The visual angle of the fovea is only about 2 degrees, the size of a dime held at arm's length. The fovea is essential for detecting both color and superfine spatial features of the environment. We track "relevant" traffic events by focusing with the fovea.

Motion and Focus for the Driver

The detail view, or the focus system, allows the driver to define the "what" and "where" while navigating the road environment. The system enables us to recognize the nature of the red light, the stop sign, and the size and details of the truck in the rear view mirror. It gives us information to tell the difference between gravel, rough road, and broken pavement, while the peripheral wide view helps us to notice the irregularity well in advance and provides critical information about how long it will take to reach it.

The wide view is one basis for detecting new hazards. It helps us to notice the "what else" and "where else"[37] when driving. In addition, the wide view defines "when" to help us manage timed events. Our ability to monitor time regulates finely coordinated motor skills, time/distance or gap estimates, and judgments about the speed of oncoming vehicles.

Learning to perform well and safely in the dynamic activity of driving means learning to effortlessly switch back and forth between the wide view and the detail view. We cannot exclude one view in favor of the other. Driving well requires focusing on a detail, defining its relevance, retaining its importance or potential importance, and moving back to the wide view. The skilled driver has learned to encode the highly detailed information that once may have overwhelmed, and to switch to see the entire field of view while remaining alert for new details that might be relevant.

States of Attention: Slow Motion and Lost Time

Zooming In *forces you to ignore new threats and disrupts timing.*

What happens when the zoom reaction kicks in? Attention narrows. Motion and new threat perception decrease. Our sense of timing is altered. When the zoom reaction starts, our ultrafast peripheral processor is put on hold. Our ability to look down the road or to the sides and gather new information away from the source of danger is immediately compromised.

Drivers who encounter the zoom reaction in an emergency say they experience a distortion in time perception that can take one of two forms: for some, events are suspended in time; for others, time is lost.[38] Some drivers report extreme clarity as events unfold in slow motion. What actually takes perhaps one or two seconds seems to take much longer. Minor but insignificant details, mostly in the central field of view, are remembered with complete clarity. The driver may execute an evasive maneuver and later be amazed that he or she had the presence of mind to calmly evaluate what to do next. The driver may also perceive events in slow motion but find that his or her reactions take too long; that is, he or she cannot take suitable action even though there seems to be plenty of time.

Alternatively, some drivers talk about the event as a blur in which time speeds up instead of slowing down. The event becomes an indistinguishable mass, a blur of a moment. Target fixation brings the threat to the foreground while the sense of timing is completely lost. Only the characteristics of the threat are remembered. Drivers on a track may follow a crash only to report later that they could not take their eyes off the unfolding calamity. A pedestrian appearing suddenly in front of the vehicle achieves an almost eerie, surreal quality. Memories of such events may persist for years.

Apparently, the ability to perceive events in slow motion can be constructive, because people are able to switch to new actions such as swerving or braking. This ability can be adaptive and influenced by training.

Exercises in Chapter 6 teach the driver to spot relevant parts of a driving scene, consciously switch between the focused and the wide view, and to formulate a visual plan of action *before* an emergency unfolds.

Motion Analysis

Our brains use at least three different kinds of motion analysis mechanisms. The first two use primitive, incredibly fast motion detection circuits to spot changes in brightness and texture. These circuits most likely use the peripheral pathways and process information without much higher-order complex thought.[39] Accordingly, these pathways are hard wired, and are not amenable to training; it is difficult to improve on a system that is extremely fast and sensitive to begin with.

However, the third kind of motion analysis mechanism, *motion relevance*, establishes higher-order neural pathways through learning (remember the "sprites" in Chapter 1). The pathways in this mechanism identify the features of objects in motion and allow us to compute how these objects are similar to or different from other objects in motion. These pathways define motion relevance in a way that's similar to how we pick out important non-moving objects in traffic. We learn to pay attention to what is important.

As a person drives down a busy boulevard, there are numerous events that the driver's brain interprets as movement: children running on a playground, workers unloading a truck, pedestrians walking, and of course the many vehicles going in the same and opposite directions. A driver has learned from experience to separate the motion events that are relevant from those that are not. He or she knows that the car approaching the stop sign from the road on the right is closing a little too fast and is not likely to make a complete stop. The driver slows in anticipation, while ignoring the movement of traffic in oncoming lanes.

Smooth Pursuit Eye Movements

Smooth pursuit eye movements allow us to track the appearance and position of moving objects when we drive. They enable us to extract detailed information from a moving object. They are performed using the focus system. If we so desire, we can effortlessly track a car merging from the right lane and know that it is a red Ford van, with two males in the front compartment. If we did not track objects with smooth pursuit eye movements, moving images would appear blurry and lack definition.

Pursuit eye movements are smooth and continuous. When the driver is tracking a target, there is constant feedback between the brain and the eye muscles to keep the target in focus. Smooth pursuit eye movements allow us to keep the image of the tracked event clear while images of untracked objects remain fuzzy. We are expertly able to separate a moving target from its background.

When you are riding as a passenger (not driving), notice that if you consciously focus on a particular sign along the side of the road and track it, the houses, trees, and buildings in the background become a blur. Your selective attention tunes in to the object you decided to track with your pursuit eye movements and tunes out other details.

Our peripheral vision and pursuit eye movements thus work together so that we perceive relevant motion. Peripheral vision gives us background information for the object of focus. The background provides relative cues for our sense of speed and influences our ability to mentally calculate the closing rates of other vehicles. The background is important for estimating the distances between vehicles and relative vehicle speeds when merging. Peripheral vision may also be essential for gauging our own speed.

Chapter 4:
Avoiding Hazards

Hazard Perception

Boris Velichkovsky and his colleagues at the Applied Cognitive Research Unit at the Dresden University of Technology, supported by BMW, have done exciting research on eye movements and hazard perception. Their studies examined dynamic eye movements, including smooth pursuit, when experienced drivers navigated an urban environment in a driving simulator (developed with the Institute of Robotics at the University of Valencia in Spain). During the experiment, potential and immediate hazards such as traffic lights or pedestrians appeared, requiring a braking reaction.

The research supports earlier hypotheses that there are two categories of *visual reaction times* to hazards: pre-attentive (ambient) and attentive (focal). When a hazard appears, there is a strong, reliable, and fast eye fixation to the threat that is twice as long as other fixations. The reaction is remarkably stable over time, even when the driving environment becomes familiar. When we spot a potential hazard, our eyes react almost instantaneously to the danger.

The reaction time for a driver's eyes to move to a hazard is about 1/10th of a second.

The switch from distributed to focused attention happens in about 100 milliseconds (1/10th of a second).[40] [41] To put the reaction time of the eyes in context, it is about four to five times *faster* than our fastest simple motor reaction to events that are staged in the lab, such as reacting to a light with a button push. When we compare the eye's response with real-world reaction times in a vehicle, the eyes react 10 to 20 times faster. We do lead with our eyes.

Drivers lock onto hazards with focused attention and direct eye movements 80% of the time. While the ambient system likely detects the hazard, the focus system takes over almost immediately, defining events that are relevant to the driver.

The average reaction times to stationary objects, pedestrians, and bicycles during daylight is approximately one second, while the average response time to such objects at night is closer to three seconds.[42] Drivers also react faster to an intruding vehicle in curves and at intersections, possibly because they are expecting a change. Older drivers are not at much of a disadvantage in terms of absolute reaction times.

The speed of our response to an intrusion varies with traffic conditions, lighting, the nature of the roadway, and our state of readiness.

The average response time to someone or something suddenly blocking the path after starting a turn in response to a green traffic signal is approximately three seconds, while the average response time to a vehicle changing one lane in daylight is about one second.

Drivers react more quickly to familiar targets.

The studies on visual reaction times show that while our eyes are capable of lightning-fast reactions, the nature of the scene and its relevance determines how fast we actually react.

We react faster to *what is important* and *what is familiar* based on our experience. Improving our ability to identify "relevant targets" and make them familiar to us in traffic will therefore speed up our reaction times.

Inattentional Blindness

Pre-attentive scene processing means to look without seeing. Pre-attentive scene processing is the mind's way of taking in a complex visual landscape without becoming overwhelmed with insignificant details. Scene processing is controlled by top down resources, or learned experiences. We attend to what *we perceive* is important based on what we've experienced in the past. Short, almost undetectable eye fixations unconsciously scan the traffic, looking for previously experienced patterns that at once help us detect whether there is safety or danger. However, we can fail to actually see, and thus exhibit *inattentional blindness* during which unexpected events are overlooked.[43]

David Strayer and his colleagues at the University of Utah presented studies on the nature and importance of pre-attentive processing while driving.[44] They examined the effects of hands-free phone conversations on simulated driving performance.

In one study, Strayer's participants drove in a simulator on a multi-lane freeway under cell phone and no cell phone conditions. Conversing on a hands-free cell phone impaired reaction times to brake lights on a lead vehicle, and the impairment became more pronounced as traffic density increased.

In a second study, Strayer's team examined how the use of a hands-free cell phone inhibited a driver's attention to the external environment. The participants drove the simulator through a background of billboards under cell phone and no cell phone conditions. To find out whether drivers' eye movements became limited or frozen when their thoughts were on a cell phone's conversation, Strayer's team measured eye fixations of the drivers in the simulator. They found that cell phone conversation did not affect the eye scan patterns and fixations. However, they did find that the cell phone affected the recognition memory of the billboards. The drivers were looking without seeing...they had inattentional blindness.

Inattention to traffic signals, brake lights ahead, and other stimuli occurs when conversing on a cell phone. The cell conversation becomes more relevant to the driver at the moment than critical visual stimuli in the scene, including brake lights of the lead vehicle.

Hazard Perception on the Road

Hazard perception is more than our eyes' quick reaction to threats. It is being able to read the road ahead and to anticipate what is going to happen in a road scene. It is the top skill that is known to predict accidents, especially in younger and older drivers. Frank McKenna and his colleagues at the University of Reading in the U.K. have conducted studies over more than a decade to compare hazard perception in experienced and beginning drivers.[45] The studies show that hazard perception is a conscious process. Expert drivers engage in *effortful* prediction and monitoring of the situation. Experienced drivers have a more accurate and sophisticated model of the driving environment, but it does not just activate automatically. According to McKenna, good hazard perception is an executive task, one that is proactive. Experienced drivers conduct more effective and efficient searches for hazards. In short, they devote more attention to obtain superior performance.

Mark Horswill is a researcher at the University of Queensland in Australia and is one of McKenna's colleagues who studies hazard perception in driving with groups of different ages and experience levels.[46] Horswill and his colleagues presented drivers with video-based hazard perception driving tests while challenging them with verbal tasks at the same time. As with many similar studies, he found that people react more slowly to hazardous situations on the road when their minds are on a verbal task. Somewhat unexpectedly, experienced drivers' reactions slowed to a much greater extent than those of novice drivers, almost bringing them down to the level of novices.

An explanation for experienced drivers' decline in response time is that verbal tasks steal away the mental concentration they need to process hazards. Unlike novices, experienced drivers normally anticipate what will happen; they read the road ahead, predict what might happen, prepare for unexpected hazards, and generally predict things in a much more sophisticated way. In contrast, novice drivers just react to situations, and do little by way of anticipation.

According to Horswill, the people with the shortest reaction times to dangerous situations in his studies are around 50 years old. Young people have much faster responses than do older people in simple lab tests, but when driving, the advantage experienced drivers gain from being able to anticipate what's going to happen completely swamps any differences in brake application times. Experience counts. The older driver knows where to look for what.

Motorcyclists and Hazards

Motorcyclists are more aware of hazards, possibly because their attention skills are better developed due to an increased sense of danger. Horswill and his colleagues assessed behaviors related to accidents in motorcyclists and in a matching group of non-motorcycling car drivers.[47] He found that motorcyclists had better hazard perception than the car drivers. While the motorcyclists and non-motorcycling car drivers did not differ on general characteristics and attitudes such as sensation seeking, social motives, and attitudes about driving or riding, motorcyclists were faster at detecting hazards.

People gain hazard perception skill with different kinds of experiences. McKenna and Horswill filmed a video simulation from a driver's-eye point-of-view. The simulation contained hazardous traffic scenes, then exactly the same scenes with the hazard removed. They then took a group of novice drivers and trained half of them in hazard perception. They found that drivers who were trained drove proportionally slower when hazards were present than they did when no hazards were present. Drivers trained in hazard perception took fewer risks.[48]

Basic Hazard Perception Skills

Detecting a hazard and moving our eyes to it is a fast and largely automatic reaction. It is particularly influenced by how familiar we are with the hazard and with the type and complexity of the traffic pattern we are in at the time. Hazard detection thus seems to work on both unconscious (preattentive) and conscious levels. The preattentive system serves as a safety net, but if our mind is elsewhere, the automatic threat warning slows; we have less attentional capacity to recognize traffic patterns and apply top down processing to the incoming stream of information. The up side is that conscious, proactive hazard perception is a skill amenable to training.

Eyes-Off Distractions

Distractions disrupt attention.[49] For example, lost with worry about a meeting with a non-performing employee, a driver misses the merge and is forced to squeeze in by speeding up and cutting someone off. Or the kids start fighting in the back seat and Mom turns for a second to shut them up and misses the truck entering from the shopping center service entrance. Or a real estate agent engaged in a cell phone conversation takes just a split second longer to notice the yellow light and jams on the brakes suddenly and gets hit from behind. All it takes is a second or two of inattention.

The majority of driver distractions are neither new nor high tech. Rather, they are aspects of everyday driving that people seldom think about—sipping a cup of coffee, changing the radio station, searching through a glove compartment, or gawking at the fender-bender on the other side of the freeway.

Jane Stutts and her colleagues at the University of North Carolina at Chapel Hill Highway Safety Research Center put three miniature video cameras in cars so that they could understand driver distractions.[50] Two of the cameras looked at the front seat area and the third was directed outside the vehicle. They found that distractions are a common part of everyday driving. A high proportion (71%) of the drivers ate or drank, 91% manipulated the music/audio controls, 46% groomed themselves, and 77% talked with passengers. Nearly all drivers manipulated vehicle controls such as windows or air conditioning and reached for objects inside the moving vehicle. About a third of the drivers used the cell phone. Certain distractions tended to occur when the vehicle was moving as well as when stopped: eating and drinking, manipulating music controls, smoking, baby and child distractions, and conversing.

Common distractions take the driver's eyes off the road for 5 to 25 seconds.

The intriguing part of the study was the in-car video's ability to capture the actual times that distractions took the drivers' attention away from the road scene. Here are the average observed times for each type of distraction:

- Adjusting music or audio: 5.5 seconds
- Putting out a smoke: 7.3 seconds
- Grooming: 11.8 seconds
- Baby and child distractions: 25 seconds
- Reaching, leaning, looking for, picking up something inside the vehicle: 7.6 seconds
- Average time to place a cell phone call: just under 13 seconds
- Average time to answer a cell phone call: just under 8 seconds

"Eye-off times" ranged from 5 to 25 seconds. This is a long time when compared to the "eye" and "traffic" reaction times discussed in the last chapter. At just 45 miles an hour, we cover approximately two football fields in 9 seconds. The difference between a collision and a safe arrival is usually far less than that.

The study also linked risky behaviors to distractions. Both answering and dialing the cell phone were associated with higher levels of "no hands on the wheel" and "eyes off the road." Preparing to eat or drink, such as unwrapping fast food or holding a cup were also linked with no hands, eyes off, and pushing into someone else's lane. Drivers could pop in a CD without lane deviation, but it still took their eyes off the road and one hand off the wheel. Reaching for objects inside the vehicle led to wandering, lane encroachment, and sudden braking.

Cell phone messages take a greater toll on complex (divided attention) tasks than on simple decisions and maneuvers in traffic.

Peter Cooper with the Insurance Corporation of British Columbia took his scientific team out of the lab and onto a live driving course to look at how distractions affect real-world driving skills.[51] They put drivers through a series of challenging driving tasks, both in the presence and the absence of voice messages.[52] Listening and responding to messages, as might occur while using a hands-free cell phone, were found to degrade driving performance on an open course. Moreover, the extent to which the messages degraded performance was connected to the complexity of the driving maneuver. Participants had twice as many errors when they were required to weave or negotiate a complex left turn than when they were simply required to stop at a light.

The more difficult and complex the cell phone conversation, the greater possible negative effect on driver distraction.[53]

Distractions disrupt a driver's attention to minor (and sometimes major) details that could be important.

A similar study on a test track showed that distractions cause drivers to miss more red lights. When distracted drivers react to a red light, they do so later, and to compensate for the delay, they brake more intensely.[54]

Distracted drivers take more risks. Distractions cause a reduction in hazard perception.

Distractions cause drivers to take more risks. In one video simulation, drivers given verbal tasks similar to a conversation took more risks.[55] Distracted drivers accept more dangerous gaps when merging with a stream of traffic and are more willing to drive closer to the car in front. It would seem that a driver might increase following distance while distracted, but the opposite is true. Many drivers are simply not aware of how often or how long they take their eyes off the road.

According to the Network of Employers for Traffic Safety (NETS), driver distraction is a contributing factor in 25 to 50% of all crashes, causing an estimated 4,000 to 8,000 traffic crashes each day. According to Kathryn Lusby-Treber of NETS, as employees strive to become more productive, they are multi-tasking as they drive. That causes crashes. These crashes pose a major risk to employers and that ultimately means a risk to their companies' bottom lines. A few simple steps can reduce the risk. NETS developed the Distracted Driver Tool Kit so that employers would have a training program to enable their employees to identify potential distractions while driving and develop techniques and strategies to better manage these distractions. The Tool Kit contains a video highlighting eight scenarios of in-vehicle distractions, a Leader's Guide, a Rate-Your-Risk Quiz, incentives, and other useful tools and information. According to NETS, "The program keeps employees focused on the task at hand—driving—and reinforces that drive-time is not down-time!" (*www.trafficsafety.org*)

Is the Other Guy Distracted?

In a 2003 poll of 1,095 drivers by Mason-Dixon Polling and Research, Inc. of Washington D.C. (sponsored by the AAA, Volvo Cars of North America, and Partners for Highway Safety), only 27% of drivers believe that drivers today are driving more safely than in the past.[56] Thirty-seven percent admitted using a cell phone while driving, 14% read while driving, and 59% ate while driving.

Fifty-six percent *of the same drivers* thought that an inattentive driver was the greatest threat to driving safety. And most respondents believed that the inattentive driver must be "the other guy." Apparently, we hold an inflated estimate of our own abilities when we take our eyes off the driving task. Somehow, we feel that the cost of distractions and inattention does not apply to us.

A Partial Solution to Distractions

The amount of "off" time caused by a distraction in part determines its cost. The longer we take our eyes and mind off the road, the greater the chance is that we will not spot and respond quickly to hazards. Even with a super-fast visual system, if we occupy our attention with other events, we will respond more slowly to danger. Distractions disrupt the driver's ability *to predict* future events. They chew up those precious seconds that we have to respond to hazards. If we look away from the road scene for more than two seconds, we increase the risk of a crash.

According to Jane Stutts, distraction potential goes up with both the number of times we look away from the road and the duration of each look, not just the longest time we look away. We must try to keep our eyes on the road all of the time.

Increasing our awareness of the cost of distractions is a big step in reducing our risk. Many drivers learn that adjusting the sound system or heat controls is best done when the car is stopped. If we are aware that a messy sandwich is more likely to take our eyes off the road for too long, it might be easier to wait until we can stop and eat. And if at all possible, we should take care of child chores before we leave the driveway. Any distraction that increases our reaction time to potential hazards is going to increase crash risk.

Yet we can *interrupt* a distraction and minimize those costs with a conscious glance down the road to capture the whole scene. If we can interrupt a five-second distraction with one- to two-second "scene gathering" glances, it will reduce the potential of a crash. We will explore an exercise for managing distractions in Chapter 6.

Stress, Arousal, and Attention

Think of attention as a rubber band
that can be stretched to the correct tension for
each application; too loose and it does not
hold the scene together, too tight and it snaps.
Arousal (sympathetic) and stress pull at one
end of the band, and the demands from the
situation pull at the other. The rubber band
can be adjusted rather quickly; sometimes in
a fraction of a second, sometimes over
seconds or minutes. Most of the time, the
attention band adjusts automatically without
our awareness, but we can take conscious
control of the band when we need to. Our goal
is to achieve the correct tension and balance
so that we can focus, do the task at hand,
move on to the next task, and refocus.

When the band snaps, our attention
locks up. It shuts down from overload and
primitive brain mechanisms tenaciously fixate
on the threat that started the whole process in
the first place. Our attention can't move on to
the next scene, the next traffic challenge, or
the next smooth action. In police driver
training, this target fixation is referred to as
"brain lock."

There is a dynamic interplay between
arousal, stress, demands, and the odds of
target fixation when a threat appears. Because
our attention flows from one level to another
based upon the complexity and demands of
traffic, we seem to adjust the band at will.
When demand increases, we stretch the band
a little tighter. A driver in congested traffic is
more attentive (hopefully) than a driver who is
cruising a lonely two-lane road through
farmland. Unfortunately, there's a dangerous
part of the link between arousal and attention

that lies beneath the surface: long-term stress increases the potential to stretch the band too tightly. Law enforcement accident investigators often ask police drivers who have crashed whether they were experiencing marriage, financial, or other emotional problems. Drivers with financial problems have been found to have more accidents.[57] Recent separation and divorce are associated with an increase in serous traffic accidents.[58] Stress and emotional arousal tug at one end of the rubber band. They influence all levels of information processing, from detecting cues to changing attention focus to strategic thinking.[59]

The Dimensions of Target Fixation

When our primitive brain receives an alarm, our primary sensory response is to freeze. As we have discussed, the visual equivalent of freezing is target fixation; we sustain our focus exclusively on one threat and direct all of our actions toward it. Tunnel vision is the furthest extreme of target fixation and the zoom reaction. The brainstem takes control of our perceptual functions and we are forced to use automatic fight-flight reactions to handle complex demands. The driver whose attention is drawn to the smoke from screeching tires looks just at the tires, does nothing but grip the steering wheel tighter, and fails to notice the car approaching the intersection that caused the driver in front to brake in the first place. The motorcyclist entering a curve fixates on a truck in the opposing lane that has crossed the double yellow line and heads straight for it. More often than not, our first reaction to extreme target fixation is to slam on the brakes, not knowing what else to do. The threat compels our attention and we lose conscious control.

Target fixation and tunneling increase with:

- Fear
- Vehicle speed
- Visual surprises
- Unfamiliarity—scene and situation
- Anger or upset
- Nervousness, new stimulants
- Fatigue
- Monotony
- Age

While it's easy to understand how target fixation is necessary for our survival if another person or animal is attacking us, it is more difficult to understand how it works in complex human-machine interactions. This primitive system evolved to handle single threats, and it does not serve the driver well when multiple threats arise from different sources at the same time. Likewise, many law enforcement officers must overcome target fixation because each new situation may contain more than one threat.

At its worst, target fixation becomes embedded in our memory; the fear mechanism that worked in one situation generalizes to others. The memory of the threat can be fragmented, with only key elements of the threat remembered: approaching headlights, maybe the eerie flashing of windshield wipers, intense pressure on the brake pedal, or a flash of sudden movement. In some instances the brain will store the contextual details around the threat because we automatically associate things that happen together. If you've had a crash, you might clearly remember the loud sound of metal crunching, the conversation from the news broadcast, and even what you were thinking about for dinner just moments before. Some people report an out of body experience when they recall a crash, as though they were above it all and watching the crisis unfold.

In the broader view, the more generalized and vague response to a threat protects us; we don't have to learn that each and every traffic intrusion could spell danger. Unfortunately, we are more apt to be afraid of similar threats in the future. In extreme cases, the trace memories of a car crash can precipitate post traumatic stress disorder (PTSD). After a crash, our memory of the event and the ensuing arousal can tug on the attentional rubber band.

Generally, once the body's emergency response executes, our reaction is automatic. Without training, the response is next to impossible to keep in check. However, cortical (that is, frontal cortex) learning can be applied to modulate and control the primitive reaction. If we did not have this capability, we would jump with surprise with each new hazard in traffic. Learning involves a quick focus on the threat, recognizing its pattern, having an executive plan associated with that pattern, calling the plan into short term memory, carrying out a well practiced evasive action, and importantly, moving the eyes to the next potential threat. In short, we have to overcome our bodies' natural tendency to rely on its primitive reactions through experience and training. Good drivers learn how to balance arousal and demands so that they control the tension in the rubber band.

Disorientation

Let's take a ride with a Highway Patrol cadet who is about to take his first hot laps on a closed-circuit course. He's been in the classroom for six weeks, and has absorbed more classroom instruction on driving (and laws) than most of us could tolerate.[60] He has the driving experience and skills typical of a 24-year-old, and has shown enough restraint on the road to keep relatively free of tickets and wrecks. He's also in excellent physical condition, so we're not going to offer any excuses for poor health or fitness.

Our trooper cadet is "up" for his first driving exercise. There's an air of nervous excitement in the group of about two-dozen cadets as the pre-warm-up briefing takes place in the small classroom adjacent to the track. There are about a dozen experienced North Carolina Highway Patrol troopers in the room who act as instructors. Sgt. Doug Pendergraft is roaming the room, barking orders to bring the cadets' full attention to what they are about to go through. Doug and his seasoned trainers have witnessed first-hand the carnage on the highways and they know the seriousness of the training. At first introduction, they all look like Marine Corps drill instructors, dressed in combat boots, black fatigues, and gray Highway Patrol T-shirts. Our cadet is well aware of being under the watchful eyes of his peers and of his school instructors.

The car is a Ford police cruiser, with a blue light bar, sirens, and a roll cage similar to what's in a NASCAR vehicle. The track is a 1.8 mile serpentine course with all kinds of surprises: elevation changes, blind corners, intersections, merges, off-camber curves, straights to allow speed build-up, and even several stop signs. (Similar tracks for police driver training are scattered throughout the U.S.) There is also a radio through which instructors can give remote instructions.

With an instructor riding shotgun, the cadet quickens the pace on the first few laps so that the tires start to break loose in each corner. Even though the cars are new, the frame and suspension squeak and groan under the strain of high-speed changes in lateral and forward acceleration.

As the cadet starts his track driving, he exhibits some signs of disorientation as the pace picks up, showing some degree of increased arousal. There is an increase in heart rate and sweating, and breathing becomes shallow.[61] His mouth is dry.

In his first exposure to track training, the cadet wants to get around the course as quickly as possible, so he accelerates in the straights, entering corners too fast. He hits the brakes hard, upsetting the suspension and making the steering jerky. He can't find a good line for the corner, and may actually change line midway through the corner. The sounds from the vehicle are telltale . . . high engine revs, downshifts, creaking suspension, and patchy squealing from the tires. Driver performance is jerky, not smooth. The turn is hard and the rear end fishtails on exit. The acceleration out of the corner is abrupt.

These conditions set up disorientation and attention overload for the driver. The speed is too fast for conditions (even on a track) and there is more to pay attention to than the student has time or mental capacity for. The cadet starts to hit cones, and steering remains jerky. His forearms become as tense as steel bands. His trapezius muscle that runs between shoulders and neck tightens so that his head movements are more restricted. The jerky throttle control becomes even more erratic. Most important, attention narrowing intensifies. The cadet is less aware of his instructor, and radio calls are shut out. His eyes start to focus on the hood of the car. Distractions such as cross traffic are ignored. He does not see an instructor's car approaching from a merge, and he is certainly not turning his head in anticipation of the next corner or intersection. He appears frozen in his seat. He has a death grip on the steering wheel, with his posture slightly forward using back muscles that he did not know he had. (Now that you know what to look for, you can easily observe a similar posture in nervous drivers on the freeway.)

After the first few hot laps are over, he steps out of the car, his memory of the whole scene a blur. He can remember the noise, the violence of the corners, and the fact that his heart was somewhere in his throat. He recalls vaguely that there was a lot going on and that everything seemed to lack a cohesive glue to hold it together. That's when the learning begins.

Experts such as Paul Whitsell[62] have come to expect that during an actual police pursuit, there occurs perceptual narrowing of some 70%, impaired depth perception, impaired ability to track multiple stimuli, impaired night vision, myopic orientation, impaired fine and complex motor skills, heightened influence of the somatic nervous system, potential issues of auditory and/or visual exclusion, psychotaxia, increased blood pressure, and increased heart rate.

It is an enlightening experience to ride as a passenger on a hot lap with an experienced police driving instructor. Instructors who are familiar with the cars and their test track are able to drive at the upper limits of the vehicle while having a casual conversation about their last fishing trip. They remain cool, calm, smooth, and above all else, fully oriented to their surroundings while sliding through corners at speed. In a matter of weeks, the cadets will approach a similar level of proficiency.

Disorientation is worse for a motorcycle rider, whether on the track or not. Let's take an initial lap through a level 1 California Superbike School with Keith Code. Keith has been teaching motorcyclists to ride well for 27 years and has guided more than 10,000 students to improved proficiency. He teaches the world over with classes in Australia, Indonesia, the United Kingdom and the United States *(www.superbikeschool.com)*.

When I asked Keith what telltale signs single out the less experienced from the more proficient riders, he answered, "visual orientation skills that keep them too close to the bike." According to Keith, the less-skilled rider is slightly more nervous, more distracted, pays attention to the wrong details, is less likely to follow instructions, and pays far too much attention to the controls. What sets the less skilled rider apart most from the best is a lack of confidence and the inability to steer with the head and eyes. The worst riders also keep their focus on their front tire.

Just like the cadet, when an inexperienced motorcycle rider starts track or training exercises, he is more likely to have an elevated heart rate, shallow breathing, and lots of sweating. He has trouble finding a consistent line through the corners. His forearms fatigue quickly from a death grip on the throttle and clutch. He is likely to fixate his vision on any other calamity on the track, and if another rider crashes, the risk is high that he may follow the downed rider. His lack of riding skill is characterized by his being unable to make decisions about what he is about to do in the next two or three seconds.

The rider who has gained proficiency does not fixate on targets, but according to Keith, has learned how to project his or her future location in space and convert visual cues to reference points. The skilled rider is more calm, less distracted, knows where to look, and scans his or her eyes over the entire scene, both adjacent to the bike and down the road. The rider pays less attention to the controls, has assured confidence, and steers with his or her eyes and head. The experienced rider, above all else, has learned goal-directed visual activities. In Keith's words, the experienced rider is "rapidly accessing available information and rapidly converting it to reference points." The rider has clear, clean visual routines.

Characteristics of the
Disoriented Driver or Rider

Disorientation is the loss of visual control over the immediate scene. The driver and the motorcycle rider in our examples show similar patterns of disorientation. Further, the disorientation induced during high stress training mimics patterns that are likely to occur just prior to a crash. Training to overcome disorientation is one way to reduce collision risk. These are typical characteristics of a disoriented driver or rider:

- Increased arousal, heart rate, respiration, sweating
- Nervousness, more likely to be startled
- Inability to concentrate
- Eyes focused on hood of car or on front wheel
- Jerky steering wheel movements, jerky lane control
- Muscles tense in forearms, shoulders
- Death grip on the steering wheel or throttle
- Unable to set up for corners
- Hits cones, makes critical mistakes
- Unable to make decisions
- Overwhelmed by little stuff: clutch, gears, brakes, balance
- Attention focused on a single source
- Threats perceived as nearest given priority
- Focus exclusively on road in front
- Not able to switch to the wide angle view of the scene

Eye Movement Patterns and Stress

Any driver faces the danger of becoming attentionally lost. In a simple study that we conducted on 37 Highway Patrol cadets, we administered a 15-minute computer task in a quiet indoor lab. No screeching tires, no pressure from peers. The cadets took the computerized test alone in a quiet room.[63] [64]

The task was fairly fast-paced and required the cadets to perform more than one operation at a time. We recorded their eye movements with an infrared camera. We looked at the number of fixations, the extent of movement in all directions (saccades), and the fixation duration.

At the time, the results surprised us. We expected the best scorers to have the most eye movements, based on the notion that more eye movements would mean they were gathering more information. The opposite was true: the cadets with the highest scores had fewer eye movements.

High scorers, it turned out, found targets faster, with shorter and fewer eye movements. They dwelled on correct targets a little longer. The cadets with higher scores were more efficient and calm. Poor scorers showed a panicky, disoriented "busywork" pattern with over-sampling in all areas of display. Interestingly, track instructors often use the term *busywork* to describe drivers who are not smooth.

Calm, cool drivers show fewer eye movements when the pressure increases.

Proficient driving is partially defined by fewer eye movements, less frantic searching; in short, more efficient search patterns. While the proficient driver shows more variable scanning of the entire scene, he or she knows where to look and what to look for, and moves on. They don't hang their glances on the unimportant.

Disorientation is more likely to happen when a driver doesn't know where to look or what to look for. As a result, the disorientation that can precede a crash is often characterized by an increase in visual noise and by a feeling of loss of control. It often occurs when the individual is distracted, surprised, or simply overwhelmed. Professionals who train police, ambulance, firefighters, pilots, and even air traffic controllers know that controlling disorientation is the primary goal of good training programs.

The odds of disorientation increase with the complexity of visual and cognitive demands (including stress) on the driver. Disorientation happens in both space and time: there is a restriction in the field of view (spatial frame, background, motion), and in the ability to do multi-task (timed) activities. Once it begins, the breakdown can feed on itself and intensify quickly.

Loss of Control

After a collision, persistent and annoying questions may later intrude on our thoughts. "What was I thinking just before the collision?" "Where was my attention?" "What could I have done differently to prevent the collision?" We want to understand the trauma and to learn to control our attention so it won't happen again.

A driver loses control when there are no visual routines to support the next action.

As stated earlier, disorientation is the loss of visual control over the immediate scene. Loss of visual control appears to happen between 350 milliseconds and two seconds after a threat is perceived. If a routine is not in place to transition the driver to the next visual pattern, the driver experiences frantic visual activity in a small part of the field of view, apparently as an attempt to find the relevant threat. Overcoming the disorientation is part of the learning process; drivers who are given structured exercises in advanced training report that they first must learn "where to look" before they can control the vehicle.

Several things can happen when a driver reacts automatically in the *wrong way* to a sudden crisis:

- Attention can shift to events that are the nearest to the driver. Threatening events are those perceived to do harm immediately—events close to the vehicle or the road directly in front of the vehicle.
- Attention can shift to events that are moving the fastest. Threatening events that are moving quickly will reach the driver first.
- Attention can shift to the loudest, largest, or most noticeable. Screeching brakes, the sound of a horn, or crunching metal are all

effective in narrowing a driver's attention to the source.

- Drivers who focus on the threat lose a good portion of their peripheral vision. In extreme cases, the driver may lose other senses, including hearing and balance, and perhaps most important, his or her confidence.
- Drivers can become "attentionally lost" in the scene. As a result, planned or anticipated eye movements don't occur. Looking ahead to the next group of vehicles, merging, or finding an escape route is difficult if not impossible without specific training to do so.

Narrowed Attention on the Road

You might argue that you neither spend time on a high-speed pursuit course nor on a motorcycle. So you ask, "How does tunnel vision play a role in my everyday driving experiences?"

It's true that most of the time the average driver does not have to set up for a high speed corner on a track. But there are likely to be passengers in the car, music playing, and an incoming cell call. The overload can be even greater than the professional under pressure.[65]

The beginning driver often experiences target fixation. In the first years of driving, the teen has a tendency to look at oncoming vehicles, sometimes a bit too long. The target fixation makes the driver tend to steer toward the other car or truck. Experience teaches the driver to keep his or her eyes moving as a way to avoid dangerous moves.

According to Phil Berardelli in *Safe Young Drivers*[66], the teen driver may be as tense as the cadet in our example of high speed training. The driver's posture may reflect that he or she is not accustomed to opposing or cross traffic. In particular, the young driver may be unable to spot developing congestion ahead (scan up), vehicles that may emerge from blind entranceways or parking spaces (scan left-right), impatient drivers (scan rear), and potholes (scan down). When a teen is learning to drive, even with a parent in the car, he or she slowly acquires skills to improve concentration and control.

New Research on Narrowed Attention

Recent studies compare the abilities of novice and experienced drivers. In the most basic studies, drivers sit in front of still or moving traffic scenes and are asked to respond to hazards. In more advanced studies, eye-tracking technology is used to monitor when and where a person looks as the scene unfolds on a simulator. And in the most advanced investigations, eye movements are tracked while people actually drive on rural and suburban roadways. More often than not, participants in these studies are asked to perform a divided-attention task in which they must simultaneously attend to events in the central visual field (a speedometer) and to incidental events in the periphery (traffic intrusions).

Generally speaking, as compared with novice drivers, expert drivers find important targets more efficiently, with fewer and shorter eye movements. As drivers become familiar with a route, their area of visual search is reduced and fixations are more directed to relevant cues, such as traffic signs and other vehicles.[67] [68] However, the experienced driver's eye movements are less predictable than the novice's because novices tend to fixate on the road or vehicle directly ahead.

Expert drivers find important cues more efficiently, with fewer and shorter eye movements. Novices tend to fixate on the road directly ahead.

For example, when teen drivers are first learning to drive, they are less aware of peripheral events such as road signs. Their primary task is to keep the vehicle in the lane, estimate the distances between leading and opposing traffic, and determine the speed of others relative to their own speed. The initial scene is overwhelming and details in the "wide view" are just not attended to.

Police and high school driving instructors commonly use narrative driving exercises in which the instructor encourages the student to comment out loud on the myriad signs and incidental events. The exercise is also an effective way for parents to increase their teen drivers' awareness of *relevant* information in all parts of the scene. If you are a parent, it is important *to listen to your teen* about the unfolding scene, and *not tell them* what you see.

Geoff Underwood, David Crundall, and Peter Chapman at the School of Psychology at the University of Nottingham in the U.K. recorded the eye movements of drivers with various levels of driving experience. They were able to take measures in their lab with video images of hazardous driving scenes and in fully instrumented road vehicles. [69] [70]

Dangerous scenes narrow your visual search patterns.

In one study by this team, a sample of drivers watched films of dangerous driving situations.[71] In all the drivers, dangerous scenes prompted a narrower visual search; drivers looked at threats longer, had less scanning distance, and looked at fewer events. The ability to spot peripheral or incidental targets decreased during hazardous situations, and detection was impaired for up to 1.5 seconds after a hazard appeared. (This supports the simulator research on the basics of hazard perception in Chapter 4.)

The Nottingham researchers addressed the relationship between driving experience, attentional capture, and the effective perceptual field.[72] Again, novice and experienced drivers had their eye movements monitored in a lab while they watched video recordings taken from a moving vehicle. The recordings were paused at different times and the participants were questioned on their ability to recall other road users and roadway features. Driver attention was empirically linked to eye movements; 70% of the recalled events were tied to direct eye fixations.

The eye movement analysis indicated that drivers look at hazards more often than at non-hazards, at central events more often than peripheral events, and at moving targets more than static targets. Experienced drivers recalled more incidental events. And once the novices' eye movements were drawn to an event such as a pedestrian stepping in front of the vehicle, they were more likely to disregard incidental events.

Hazard events, central events, close events, and moving events are more likely to capture our attention. Training and experience teach us to look at peripheral events.

The on-the-road research looked into the specific components of visual attention that were likely to change as drivers had more road exposure. Experienced drivers looked more often to the left and right; they varied their direction of gaze more than the novices did. Novices tended to look directly ahead, with long gazes on the road itself or the vehicle directly ahead. For example, on rural roads the novices showed a simple pattern of eye fixations: regardless of where they looked at one moment, at the next moment they tended to look at the road far ahead. The experienced drivers, in contrast, showed a more variable scan pattern; there was less evidence of the dominance of viewing the road ahead and there was continual inspection of all parts of the scene.

Experienced drivers may glance far ahead, but they break up target fixation with frequent glances to the left and right and to the mirrors. The road far ahead is a compelling target for all drivers, but the novices are about twice as likely to get stuck on this one scanning strategy. In contrast, experienced drivers' scanning behavior was characterized as sensitive to whatever traffic conditions prevailed.

Experienced drivers monitor other road users and frequently *switch their attention* to all parts of the scene. Driving instructors teach that the further ahead a driver scans left and right, fewer "surprises" occur and planning time is increased.[73] Planning ahead and anticipation shorten the necessary reaction time to threats.

Chapter 5:
New Learning and the Future

The future. Teen drivers will learn to scan more effectively by playing video games that direct eye movements to critical hazards. The games will not only be able to guide the new drivers to when and where hazards occur, they will register reaction times to complex events, incrementally monitoring how the driver pays attention to dash displays and different parts of the road scene at the same time. The games will allow high school instructors to track attentional skill development in each student. If the student is deficient in one skill, feedback and practice will build the skill so that the student can move on to more complex challenges. Sometimes the structured feedback will be hands-on with a driving instructor who has access to the game scores, at other times it will be automatic via the software itself. Once basic perceptual/cognitive skills are documented, more advanced training will be introduced.

More advanced software will point out to both the instructor and student areas that need work: glancing at mirrors, gap selection, smooth acceleration and stopping, turning smoothly, maintaining traffic position and speed, judging intersections and approaching traffic, coordinating merges, spotting pedestrians and bicyclists, and avoiding surface hazards. In advanced levels of play, the student will be able to get an exact profile of how each unique distraction, such as popping in a CD or chatting with folks in the back seat, will compromise his or her ability to do these tasks essential to good driving. (Please go to *www.disciplined-attention.com* for links to simulator and training sites.)

If this sounds too futuristic, it's not. Much of it is here now. Hazard perception tests are already a compulsory part of the official driving test in the United Kingdom (as of November 2002) and in most states in Australia.[74]

Basic Cognitive Skills — Assessing the Field of View

It is now well established in the scientific community that older drivers who have a measurable restriction in their functional field of view are more prone to highway accidents.[75] The Useful Field of View (UFOV)® is a computerized test that measures the speed at which individuals can process information within a 30° arc in all directions of the visual field under a variety of cognitively demanding conditions, including divided attention and finding targets against complex backgrounds. The test presents faster and faster display screens while it measures the area from which one can extract visual information in a single glance without eye or head movements. The test literally searches for the speed and decision making limits of the driver. Because of the precise nature of the test, the targets do not move as in a video simulation.

Over the last 25 years, much of the research on elderly drivers has been spearheaded by Karlene Ball and her colleagues at the University of Alabama at Birmingham. In a long series of well-controlled studies, they have mapped out how older drivers sometimes lose the ability to gather information from the periphery, especially when they are required to do more than one thing at a time.[76] Karlene uses the UFOV® test to measure an individual's window of attention. The UFOV test is fully described at *www.visualawareness.com.* The research is groundbreaking because it is the first to link a driver's restriction in functional field of view to an elevated risk of crashes on the highway.

Dan Roenker and his colleagues at Western Kentucky University adopted the UFOV for use as a training program rather than a test for a group of elderly adults (average age 69).[77] This goes back to our observation in Chapter 4 that training in basic perceptual/cognitive skills can improve driving performance. Roenker's software focused on individualized practice for fundamental skills such as speed of processing and expanding the field of view in complex displays. However, the training did not include a virtual representation of driving and some participants even questioned its relevance to driving.

To see how the basic training fared, it was compared to a matched group of drivers who received training in a driving simulator commonly used for police training. The simulator was fixed-base (no vehicle suspension) with steering wheel, brake, accelerator pedals and an instrumented dashboard in which a driving scene was

projected onto three screens of central and
peripheral traffic views
(*www.doronprecision.com*).

The study first screened a large number
of drivers and those with a 30% reduction in
their field of view (high risk) were assigned to
one of two groups: expanding the field of view
training or traditional simulator training. A
control group without field of view deficits was
a "low risk" group. The study thus pre-
selected drivers who had a compromised field
of view.

The study is unique because the
computerized measures were then compared
with actual road performance. The driving
course had two 7-mile loops of
urban/suburban roadway. The evaluators
looked at how well the drivers maintained lane
position, activated turn signals, stopped
smoothly, turned, maintained speed, and
maintained position in traffic. They also noted
whether the older drivers committed
dangerous maneuvers, including failing to
scan intersections for traffic control devices
and making inadvisable turns across traffic.

The results showed a picture of driver
improvements that matched the type of
training received. The older drivers in the
study drove cautiously and errors were not
frequent; nevertheless, simulator training
improved turning into the correct lane and
signal usage, but the effects dissipated after
18 months, the limits of the study. By
comparison, four hours of the computerized
training that reinforced expanding the field of
view reduced dangerous maneuvers on the
road and persisted out to 18 months.

Using low cost training to expand the
field of view is not limited to older drivers. A

recent study explored how we can expand young drivers' attention through video games. Scientists from the Department of Cognitive Sciences Center for Visual Science at the University of Rochester looked at the extent to which playing video games influenced attentional capacity in people between 18 and 23.[78] The study is important because it shows that perceptual learning though action video game playing was *not* task specific. When the participants learned to multi-task under pressure during games such as *Grand Theft Auto3, Half-Life, Counter Strike, Crazy Taxi* and others, the skill carried over to other tasks related to a driver's capacity, including the UFOV test.

The study tracked the skills of men who played the action video games at least four days per week for a minimum of one hour per day. Playing produced enhanced attention over the visual field even at locations beyond those included in the original games. The studies also looked at the *timing* characteristics of visual attention and found that the pressure to act rapidly during the action video games improved the ability to process items over time by reducing bottlenecks of attention. Unfortunately, the study did not look at actual driving behavior on the road.

Donald Fisher and his colleagues at the University of Massachusetts at Amherst used a fixed-base driving simulator to examine the effect of both experience on the road and PC-based awareness training on younger drivers' performance in risky traffic scenarios.[79] They ran three groups of drivers on the simulator: one group of novice drivers trained on the PC, and two groups who received no PC training.

The PC-based awareness program was the
AAA Foundation for Traffic Safety product
called Driver ZED (Zero Errors Driving)™.[80]
The testing simulators presented three virtual
worlds of roadway scenes that stretched over
5 miles each.

Young drivers who were given PC-based
training drove more cautiously in the
simulator. The study is notable because the
PC training reinforced conscious planning for
novel traffic scenarios in which the drivers
had to *predict* what might come into view, but
was not yet in view. Overall, the younger,
inexperienced drivers who were trained on a
PC operated their vehicles in risky scenarios
in ways that differed measurably from those of
untrained, younger inexperienced drivers.
Driving behavior on the simulator became
similar to that of experienced drivers.

Video Training for Specific Skills

Beginning drivers are given brief video
training to spot road hazards. What specific
visual skills transfer to driving on the road?
Can we train drivers to actually scan more
effectively and move their eyes to new targets?
A study by Peter Chapman and his colleagues
at the University of Nottingham introduced
new drivers to video training that reinforced
scanning for potential dangers in multiple
locations in the visual scene.[81] Subsequently,
the scientific team monitored the drivers' eye
movements both when they watched new
videos *and when they drove.*

The video training was less than an
hour long and elegantly simple. The training
taught visual search strategies, knowledge of

the road environment, how to scan for new information and how to anticipate the traffic ahead.

Initially, the drivers watched scenes of dangerous driving situations and simply gave a running commentary of what they were looking at (narrative driving). They also pushed a button as soon as they detected dangers in the situation. Next the drivers looked at new video clips of dangerous scenes, but the clips were played at half speed to give the driver plenty of time to anticipate what would happen next. A widened visual search was encouraged by having critical parts of the scene highlighted, with a special emphasis on dangerous events. Then the drivers watched the clips again and listened to an expert comment on why specific hazards were important.

The trained drivers showed a greater spread of horizontal search both immediately after training and at follow-up. As in similar studies, all drivers held their gaze longer on dangers. However, the drivers who were trained with video hazard detection had shorter threat gazes immediately after training. They looked at hazards but moved on.

Drivers who had the video training also showed a greater spread of horizontal search (scanning) on the road. The drivers who received the video training were less likely to tunnel on a threat in subsequent videos. They were able to process threat information faster. As an added bonus, drivers exposed to the video training extended their search strategies and kept their eyes moving faster even when no hazards were present.

The control group showed no changes in visual search patterns over the first six months of driving. They did not find targets faster than when they started driving. They also did not expand their visual search after experience on the road. Beginning drivers who receive scanning and hazard awareness training through video experiences may subsequently use a *more conscious scanning strategy* than drivers without the video experience.

The Case for Varied Training

Acquiring skills, practicing skills, and, in fact, sustaining skills can be achieved in different training environments with different methods and tools for each step in the process. Since driving is an extremely complex activity, there are many tools at our disposal. For example, the Raydon Virtual Driver™ (RVD) is a fully interactive driving simulator for driver education and driver improvement courses. The RVD™ employs established, standardized curricula developed with leading traffic safety organizations, including the National Safety Council and the American Driver and Traffic Safety Education Organization, to instruct drivers on safe and proper driving procedures (*www.virtualdriver.net*).

Class instruction, reading, and accessing web pages familiarize the driver with knowledge as a basis for acquiring and practicing new skills. And as the new studies show, video game and virtual training can be a part of learning to drive; learning to move the eyes and multitask with exclusive attention on

the driving scene are good lessons. But drivers
also need hands-on instruction and live
experiences to fully develop time sharing skills
that might be needed in an emergency.
Simulator or video game training cannot
totally replace live training. Video games are
limited in that they presently cannot teach the
driver to look ahead. Live experience pushes
the student to handle more complex visual
situations. Practice under more challenging
and stressful conditions hones the driver's
ability to control the zoom reaction. If
simulator or classroom training does not teach
control of the zoom reaction, it has limited
utility to train for unexpected emergencies.

*We need to give drivers access to the
entire toolkit to enhance driving skills.*

Chapter 6: Exercises

Disclaimer

The suggested exercises in Chapter 6 are designed to help you move your eyes to all parts of the traffic scene and gather more information. **It is important that you first do these exercises as a passenger in the front seat of a vehicle.** It is also important that when you drive, you practice these exercises under safe traffic conditions.

If you get behind the wheel of a vehicle and start to practice **all** of the suggested exercises in Chapter 6 at once, you can become overwhelmed and not pay attention to the driving task. Take the exercises one at a time and practice them in safe, non-congested settings.

The reader must take reasonable care when using the suggestions and acting on the contents of this book. Profile Press will not accept liability for any injuries or damages caused to the reader that may result from the reader's acting upon or using the content contained in *Disciplined Attention*.

Specific Warnings

- **Exercise 1. The Two-Second Life Saver:** this exercise is designed to encourage you to take a second glance at traffic before you make a move. There are situations in which taking the time for a second glance can cause you to impede traffic and increase the odds of a crash. Use your judgment before you take a second glance.

- **Exercise 2. Expansion:** this exercise trains you to move your eyes to all parts of a scene. When you first learn to move your eyes to all parts of a scene, there is a risk that you will unconsciously also move your hands. This is especially true for novice and teen drivers. Unconscious hand movement may cause unwanted steering wheel movements and a possible crash. Please do the exercises in a safe environment such as an empty parking lot until you are comfortable with them.

- **Exercise 5. Narrative Driving:** talking can be a distracting activity and can take your focus off of the traffic conditions present at the time. Practice narrative driving in a safe setting with a passenger who is also watching the road. This warning is particularly important for teens. Practice narrative driving with an instructor or parent in the front seat who is also acting as a lookout for hazards and traffic conditions.

- **Exercise 6. Managing Distractions:** the two-second rule is the *maximum* time that you should take your eyes off of traffic, but even two seconds can be dangerous. It is best to keep your eyes on traffic at all times. Allowing yourself to repeatedly take your eyes off of traffic for consecutive breaks can be dangerous and lead to bad habits.

- **Exercise 8. The Eyes Lead:** looking all the way through the corner or intersection can cause you to look too far ahead and make you ignore events that are close to the vehicle. Looking too far ahead can cause you to be inattentive to pedestrians, bicyclists, and traffic close to your vehicle. First, practice by looking through a corner or intersection in uncongested traffic conditions. Don't forget to look both "far" and "near" to your vehicle before taking an action. As discussed in Chapter 1, don't use the racing practice of looking way down the road so that you exclude events that are close to the vehicle.

- **Exercise 9. The Visual Plan:** please keep your attention on traffic conditions around you at all times. Don't get lost in thought about possible escape routes and forget to pay attention to current traffic conditions.

Using the Exercises

These exercises are designed to foster communication between parent and teen, instructor and student, and friend and supporter. The skills that are developed will soon become automatic when driving.

Introduction

Like playing sports, operating a complex production line, or managing a department, disciplined attention is a learned skill. By consciously directing your eye movements to relevant and diverse targets during calm moments in traffic, you produce more efficient search patterns. Efficient search patterns free up your attention so that when new information enters the scene, you are less likely to be surprised and caught off guard.

After you have learned them as a passenger, practice these exercises every time you drive, even if it's only for a few minutes at a time. Disciplined attention will soon become automatic; you will be carrying out informative glances to all parts of the scene unconsciously. Take time to go back every few months and read over the suggestions again. Practice the ones that have not yet become part of your driving routine. Like any other learned skill, disciplined attention improves with practice. It also confers a positive sense of mastery and control over your driving.

As discussed in the opening pages, these exercises have both research and practical origins, but they are not carved in stone. As you go through the exercises, make note of those that are helpful and those that are not. At the end, we would appreciate your sending us feedback, which will be valuable to other drivers. Please provide feedback to other drivers through *www.disciplined-attention.com.*

The Four Stages

The path to disciplined attention can be thought of as having four stages:

1. Becoming familiar with new hazards
2. Reinforcing hazard awareness
3. Anticipating and predicting
4. Taking control of your attention

It is important to reiterate that many of these exercises introduce new skills and should only be attempted when you are a passenger in the front seat of a vehicle. Please don't try them for the first time when you are driving because they will take your mind off of the driving task and could lead to a crash.

The first set of exercises encourages you to expand your effective field of view and become aware of the hazards throughout your visual field. You will learn to move your eyes over the scene just as a professional driver does. You will learn what to look for, where to look, and how you can improve your ability to the see "what else" and "where else" that have the potential to turn into threats.

The second set of exercises explores ways to reinforce your new seeing habits and encourage you to share your new skills with friends, family, and co-workers. You will be coached in switching your attention between the focused and the wide view, and you will learn about the cost of distractions.

The third set of exercises allows you to take control of your visual attention. You will use the technique used by professional drivers, to "lead with your eyes." You will learn to look all the way through intersections, corners, and turns so that your actions become smooth and predictable to other drivers. You will also learn to formulate evasive actions and ultimately become skilled at predicting the dangerous actions of others.

In the final exercises, you will take control of your visual attention as a full time process when you drive. You will learn why to control your emotions and remain calm when confronted with aggressive driving styles. You will learn to predict, instead of being surprised by the actions of other drivers.

When you reach the end of the exercises, you will start the transition from a driver who must rely on primitive and sometimes dangerous instinctive reactions to a driver who has acquired and practiced the skills necessary to remain calm in an unexpected traffic situation.

Baseline: The Unaware Driver

- Relies on instinctive reactions, easily surprised by hazards.
- Hazards produce target fixation (tunneling) and information gathering is primarily in the central (focal) field of view.
- Less able to detect incidental or peripheral events.
- Drawn to events that are moving, near vehicle, or directly ahead.
- Easily distracted by things inside and outside of the vehicle.
- Not aware of the time cost of distractions.
- Distractions are for long intervals, greater than two seconds.

Stage 1:

Becoming Familiar with New Hazards— Expanding Your Effective Field of View Exercises:

1. **Two-Second Life Saver:** the power of the two-second glance.
2. **Expansion:** eyes on all parts of the scene.
3. **Relevance:** focus on what and where.
4. **Relevant Movement:** what else, where else, and when.

Stage 2:

Reinforcing Hazard Awareness Exercises:

5. **Narrative Driving:** talking it out with a partner.
6. **Managing Distractions:** the "eyes off" limits.
7. **Conscious Switching**: alternating the focused and the wide view.

Stage 3:

Advanced Awareness — Anticipate and Predict Exercises:

8. **The Eyes Lead:** eyes through corners, intersections, and turns.
9. **The Visual Plan**: formulating a way out.

10. **Anticipate and Predict:** anticipating the action of others and staying cool.

Stage 4:

The Aware Driver

- Practice leads to automatic awareness and unconscious informative glances.
- Taking control of your visual attention.

Table 1. The Stages of Attention Development and Exercises

Stage	Exercise	Goal
Stage 1. Becoming Familiar with New Hazards—Expanding Your Effective Field of View	1. The Two-Second Life Saver	Improve information gathering capabilities with each glance and move on to new targets.
	2. Expansion	Learn to look to all parts of the visual field.
	3. Relevance	Become familiar with relevant events.
	4. Relevant Movement	Distinguish moving events that could be important.
Stage 2. Reinforcing Hazard Awareness	5. Narrative Driving	Share your visual attention learning with family and friends.
	6. Managing Distractions	Become aware that distractions cost precious seconds of attention.
	7. Conscious Switching	Learn to use both visual systems to your advantage.

Table 1 – continued

Progress	Sports Application
Does your short term memory for road scenes improve?	Snapshot vision is the ability to gather information about a scene in a glance. Focus is being able to pick and choose relevant and familiar targets (reference points) and getting the eyes to move on.
Are you spotting new hazards that are not directly in front of your vehicle?	Look for opponent's eye movements, foot movements, posture, etc. Scan the scene to warm up. Learn to calm with eye movements. Introduces mastery over the scene.
Are you learning to focus on new events that might be potential hazards?	Defining relevance is one way to achieve focus. Familiarity breeds faster reaction times and eliminates surprise (and target fixation).
Are you able to tell what is important movement and what is not?	Use your ambient and focal systems to define what's moving into the scene that's important and what's not. Help develop "sprites."
Do you discuss how you are more attentive to various features of the traffic environment?	Narrative sharing is talk with the coach, the players' meeting, or conversation with a teammate after a play. It's the cognitive exercise that crystallizes your visual attention, what you see and don't see, and how you will improve your eye and attention patterns on the next play. It's the basis of learning new moves. It identifies the visual routines you need to work on.
Are you engaging in fewer distracting activities when you drive? Do you take your eyes off the road less often and for less time?	Managing distractions is the essence of a professional competitor's true focus. Staying in the visual moment or "in the now."
Are you aware of using your focal and ambient systems to gather different types of information?	Conscious switching is the antidote to target fixation in the middle of a high intensity move.

Table 1 – continued

Stage	Exercise	Goal
Stage 3. Advanced Awareness— Anticipate and Predict	8. The Eyes Lead	Look through corners, intersections, and traffic pathways before action.
	9. The Visual Plan	Formulate an escape route before an emergency arises.
	10. Anticipate and Predict	Use your eyes and attention to anticipate and predict the moves of other drivers.
Stage 4. The Aware Driver	Taking Control of Visual Attention	Enjoy your new eye and attention skills. Enjoy driving and being alert all of the time.

Table 1 – continued

Progress	Sports Application
Do you consciously move your eyes through most of your traffic moves?	The eyes lead by looking beyond the play and visualizing you and your opponent's path of travel. It is mental follow through.
Has your strategic planning improved?	Visualize the entire play to reduce the odds of surprise and emotional arousal. Visualize your eye movements and these become routines. Pre-practice the eye patterns that are important to each play. Follow the dots.
Are you less surprised by the moves of other drivers?	The ability to anticipate and predict follows not being surprised, upset, or angry.
Is driving more stress free and relaxing? Are you less angry on the road? Is driving more fun?	Staying calm and poised, anticipating and predicting, expands your effective field of view. Getting upset or angry restricts your field of view and causes more mistakes.

Baseline Assessment

Before you work through the stages of exercises, take a few minutes to answer some questions about your driving. Please circle the answer (number score) that applies to you.

1. When you are in a line of traffic, do you find yourself fixating straight ahead:

a. at the car in front of you?

never (3)   rarely (2)   sometimes (1)   frequently (0)

b. at the lane between cars?

never (3)   rarely (2)   sometimes (1)   frequently (0)

c. at the road far ahead?

never (3)   rarely (2)   sometimes (1)   frequently (0)

2. While driving, do you:

   a. eat?

      never (3)   rarely (2)   sometimes (1)   frequently (0)

   b. groom?

      never (3)   rarely (2)   sometimes (1)   frequently (0)

   c. dial the cell phone?

      never (3)   rarely (2)   sometimes (1)   frequently (0)

   d. talk on the cell phone?

      never (3)   rarely (2)   sometimes (1)   frequently (0)

3. Are you likely to be overwhelmed at busy intersections with heavy cross traffic?

never (3)   rarely (2)   sometimes (1)   frequently (0)

4. Do you take your eyes off the road for more than two seconds at a time to take care of tasks inside the vehicle?

(Note: many drivers are simply not aware of how long they take their eyes off the road, so take a few seconds to think about your answer.)

never (3)   rarely (2)   sometimes (1)   frequently (0)

5. Do you share your skills at spotting new road hazards with someone else?

never (0)   rarely (1)   sometimes (2)   frequently (3)

6. Do you sometimes take a second glance at the traffic scene before committing to an action?

    never (0)   rarely (1)   sometimes (2)   frequently (3)

7. Do you steer:

a. with your head?

    never (0)   rarely (1)   sometimes (2)   frequently (3)

b. with your eyes?

    never (0)   rarely (1)   sometimes (2)   frequently (3)

8. Do you use low demand traffic moments to formulate escape routes?

    never (0)   rarely (1)   sometimes (2)   frequently (3)

Ken Mills

9. When you are stopped waiting to make a left turn, do you take the time to consciously look all the way through the intersection and visualize what your path will be?

never (0)   rarely (1)   sometimes (2)   frequently (3)

10. Do the moves of other drivers leave you upset or angry?

never (3)   rarely (2)   sometimes (1)   frequently (0)

11. Do you view your morning or evening commute during rush hour as:

a time of urgency and stress (0)   a time to listen to the news (1)

a time to relax and listen to music (2)   a time to think quietly (3)

Tally up the number score for each item. If you scored above 40, you practice disciplined attention.

Stage 1: Becoming Familiar with New Hazards—Expanding Your Effective Field of View

Exercise 1. The Two-Second Life Saver

Warning: Do this exercise only while you are a passenger in the front seat.

Problem:
Rushing into a complex traffic situation before you have a complete picture may result in your becoming "attentionally lost" and might cause you to miss important visual information. Trying to take in too much, too fast is a sure way to increase random chaotic eye movements and scatter your attention. Most drivers underestimate how much information they can gather with short *focused* glances into the driving scene.

Solution:
The first few seconds of scene processing are the most valuable to the driver. Let your eyes take in the scene for a few seconds longer than you normally would *before you commit* to an action. Concentrating on the scene for a second or two develops your ability to gather a large amount of information in a quick glance and improves your short-term memory (STM). It is a learned skill. For example, rolling stops don't allow you to take in the whole scene. They keep the background moving and then it is more difficult to spot a pedestrian or wrong-way bicyclist. Stopping gives you an extra precious second of visual information. Also, taking a few seconds to gather scene information reinforces the habit

of slowing down when your visual field is restricted by hills, congestion, rain, fog, and snow.

Quarterbacks are trained to gather a snapshot view of the defense before launching a pass. Competitive skiers take a quick view of the downhill before leaving the gates. Highway Patrol troopers can take a quick look at a busy intersection and give a remarkably detailed commentary about what is happening and what is about to unfold. Just as we're not great at remembering details about events to which we're not paying attention, with practice we can get quite good at remembering details about events to which we *are* paying attention.

Take a second glance.
Give your eyes time to focus.

Exercise:
Do this exercise only while you are a passenger in the front seat.

Take a snapshot of the road by looking down the road for just two seconds, then close your eyes. Wait five seconds, and then report everything that you saw to the driver. Repeat three times. Are you gathering more information with each glance? What did you miss that might have been important? Practice this step every time you are a passenger (and the driver is willing), until you can take in everything you need to know in two seconds or less.

Caution: When you are driving, the two-second rule applies **only** to developing your attention and eye movement patterns, not to look-ahead strategies or following distances. The traditional advice is to scan 12 (or 10 or eight) seconds ahead; this encourages you to anticipate where the vehicle will be in that time, while mapping the road ahead. **This is good advice.** At 60 mph, that may be about 1,000 feet ahead of your vehicle. However, it may take you only two seconds or less to gather information about the path that your vehicle will take over the next eight to 12 seconds. Your brain works at a speed that is much faster than any roadway vehicle. Use that faster speed to your advantage. Don't forget that conditions in traffic can change rapidly and you may have to update your two-second glance often.

Do not use the two-second rule to determine following distances in traffic. If you know that you can gather all the scene information you need with a two-second glance, it does **not** mean that you can follow another vehicle with only a two-second gap. When a collision starts to unfold, it takes about a half-second to identify the hazard, and depending on the complexity of the situation, another one to three seconds to react. Our motor movements are not nearly as fast as our perceptual processes. Many professional driving instructors recommend a two-second gap as the minimum, and a four-second gap as the maximum if traffic allows. In rain, the gap minimum is four seconds, and in snow and ice it is four to six seconds.

Exercise 2. Expansion

Problem:

We take our peripheral vision for granted and tend not to consciously move our eyes to all parts of the scene. In simple situations with only a single threat, relying on peripheral vision might be adequate; but in a complex, fast-paced driving environment we need to develop new strategies to assess threats from all parts of the visual field. Problems while driving can come from the edges of our visual field. Cars entering from hidden driveways come out of nowhere. Children dart into the road and simply appear. To make matters worse, television, movies, and computer habits train us to focus on the center of the screen.

Solution:

Expanding field of view is a conscious process that can improve performance in drivers of all ages. If you learn to look more to the sides and about 100 feet wider than the street, you will start to pick up new hazards. It is a simple process that yields immediate results, whether you are on a peaceful country road or a congested freeway. At first, expanding your field of view is a conscious process that may produce some unwanted hand and vehicle movements. Over time, you will gradually learn to move your eyes without moving your hands.

The first exercise (the Two-Second Life Saver) guided you to increase the amount of information you could gather with a static, focused glance. This second exercise (Expansion) builds on Exercise 1 and encourages you to move your eyes to all parts of the scene. Moving your eyes expands your information gathering abilities exponentially.

Move your eyes to new targets in all parts of the scene.

Do not depend on peripheral vision to gather important information.

The contents of a complex driving scene can be captured by deliberately moving your eyes to all parts of the scene. Your eyes and mind can focus on a different portion of a scene about every ¼ second, and each fixation gathers a tremendous amount of information.

As an added bonus, when you practice moving your eyes to all parts of the scene, you also increase the amount of information gathered by your peripheral vision. This greatly expands your effective field of view.

Exercise:
Do this exercise only while you are a passenger in the front seat.

This exercise reinforces moving your eyes to all parts of the scene. It also encourages you to move your head. (This exercise is particularly useful to law enforcement personnel on patrol.)

Talk about what you are seeing while you sit in the front seat as the passenger. After you have looked, describe in detail the other vehicles, the road surface, objects at the side of the road, and what other vehicles are doing.

Set aside four to eight seconds and consciously move your eyes to all parts of the scene. Move your head. Look left, right, up, and down. Don't forget to turn your head so that you check out traffic approaching from the rear in adjacent lanes.

Practice this exercise at least three times each time you get into a car as a passenger. It is good to have reminders, such as stop signs or exit signs, which will prompt you to consciously expand your field of view. Thus, every time you see your reminders, *and if it's safe to do so,* set aside four seconds to consciously move your eyes to all parts of the scene. Select specific targets and count the targets. Observe everything about the immediate scene. If you are comfortable with four seconds of scanning, try increasing your scanning time according to the traffic situation. Start the scene scan for four seconds, move it out to six, and then to eight seconds. Look to all parts of the scene with each increase in time, and don't forget to look up, down, left, and right.

Sometimes, a glance is not enough to gather critical information. Turning your head is a learned skill that is essential in gathering more information. Turning your head before you change lanes ensures that there is a space for you to go. Turning your head, focusing, and estimating the speed of approaching traffic gives you more accurate information than just using peripheral vision to estimate speed. Turning your head and using two-second glance skills (Exercise 1) allows you to gather information about cars adjacent to you and in cross traffic.

If you remember to scan the scene three times for eight seconds each time, you have invested less than a half a minute in improving your visual attention.

Exercise 3. Relevance

Problem:
We instinctively pay attention to the road or vehicles directly ahead, the center of the visual field, obvious hazards, or objects in motion. However, relevant traffic events are neither obvious nor always directly ahead. Hazards can and will appear in all parts of the driving scene.

Solution:
Knowing what events are relevant in the driving scene is learned knowledge, a top down process (Chapter 3). Experienced drivers do not predictably just look ahead for obvious hazards, they *consciously* look to all parts of the visual field for relevant events. The proficient driver learns to become familiar with hazards because it is a critical step in anticipating them.

Paying attention to relevant traffic elements overcomes inattentional blindness. There are many flashing red brake lights that you have learned to ignore. However, the driver who is watching for brake lights **and** changes in the distance between their vehicle and the one ahead is more likely to brake in time to avoid a rear end collision. Proficiency results in our learning the following:

- *You look at what you know.* Drivers who consciously make an effort to become aware of hazards will be more likely to see them when it really counts.
- *You react faster to the familiar.* Once you are aware of a hazard, your eyes' reaction times will be faster to a

similar hazard when encountered later. The lack of time to react to a hazard is the first stage of a crash. It takes time and distance to bring a vehicle to a stop, and that extra second of visual reaction time can make a big difference.

- *Relevant cues are not necessarily the most attention-grabbing.* Good drivers know where to look and what to look for. If their eyes are lost in looking for a relevant target during an emergency, the appropriate response may come too late or not at all.
- *You can avoid a hazard if you anticipate it.* Your deliberate attention to hazards dramatically improves the odds that you will avoid them.
- *Relevance changes with the situation at hand.* Your experience and practice at spotting hazards in varying traffic conditions will make you a better driver.

The proficient driver consciously pays attention to the targets that are important in the immediate situation; the edge of the road, a merge sign, a traffic sign just at the crest of the hill, etc. Next, the locations of the targets are noted (put into short term memory) and, with practice, the target becomes integrated into a maneuver. When drivers take track schools in which visual cues are consistent lap after lap, they soon integrate into their actions the visual reference points for each corner. While the driver may start with a wide view of each corner, he or she soon learns to move his or her eyes through the corner, smoothly tracking each target as it is needed, then discarding it as a new target is acquired. On the road, the process is similar, but much more difficult. There is cross traffic; there are potholes, pedestrians, bicyclists, and more unexpected surprises. The professional driver learns to look ahead at the whole scene, but also reserves informative glances in all directions to stay safe. Will that truck drift over into my lane? Is the intersection going to be clear in the next few seconds, even though I have the right of way? Transforming the unexpected to the expected involves consciously looking at targets in the traffic scene and deciding whether they are relevant.

Exercise:
Focus on what and where, and learn which visual targets are relevant in traffic.

As in Exercise 2, Expansion, *when you are a passenger,* set aside four seconds to scan the entire traffic scene in front of you and in your mirrors, but focus only on targets that are relevant to your driving.

What: Learn to look for events that are relevant to your driving and ignore events that are not. **Relevance is defined by the task at hand.** Relevant targets include road signs, the apex of the curve, gravel in roadway, fog, the white line on right side of road, potholes, merging traffic, pedestrians in a crosswalk, brake lights, intersections, and turn signals. Ask yourself, could the object or event be important to my survival? Could it become a hazard?

- Locate irrelevant cues, such as billboards, business signs, license

plates, or the model of the car next to
you, and move on.
• Distinguish between the obvious
  (flashing, moving, bright) and the
  truly important (merging vehicle,
  pathway through intersection,
  approaching gaps in traffic).

Where: Learn to look for events that are
relevant and not part of your central field of
view. Try to locate objects or events in **all**
parts of the visual field. Don't restrict your
search for relevant targets just to the view
directly in front of you. Where in the scene
can relevant events appear? Down for road
hazards? Left for oncoming traffic? Left for
cars approaching an intersection too fast?
Right for pedestrians about to cross against
the light? Up for signals? Look for relevant
cues at the edges of the roadway, in the rear
view and side mirrors.

Exercise 4. Relevant Movement

Problem:
Without training, the motion detection pathways in our brains work in the background. When acting in a background processing mode, most drivers do not instinctively make a distinction between motion that is relevant and motion that is not.

Solution:
Learn to identify motion that is relevant to the driving scene. We respond instinctively to objects in motion; they grab our attention more compellingly than anything else. This motion detection system is well developed and works automatically, without conscious thought. If several objects are in motion, the one that is moving differently—faster, slower, in a different direction—will get our attention.

As a potential collision scene unfolds, it is almost certain that critical cues will be moving: vehicles or pedestrians approaching from the side, a truck approaching too fast from the rear, or a car about to run a red light. Yet the object that presents the greatest hazard *may not be the one that grabs our attention.* Here are some exercises to improve how you spot **relevant moving** targets.

Exercise:
Focus on what else, where else, and when, and learn which motion is relevant to you in traffic.

When you are a passenger, set aside 10 seconds and scan the entire traffic scene ahead and in the side mirror. Ask yourself what moving events are going to influence the driver's next actions. Will the cars moving in the opposite direction influence a merge? Will cars moving in your direction be affected if the driver changes direction suddenly?

What else: What moving cues are you aware of in your direct line of sight? What are you locking on to? Are you able to keep your eyes moving to new targets? Do some aspects of motion in your central field of view keep you fixated on particular targets? Are you able to consciously move away from those attractive targets and look for other moving targets?

Where else: What moving cues that are not in your direct line of sight are grabbing your attention? What makes your eyes move? Color? Speed? Notice how quickly you pick up any motion in the periphery. Can you train yourself to look at these motion cues and focus back on traffic?

When: Notice that when you are looking to perform a turn into traffic, you are unconsciously timing the approach of other vehicles. What is the size of the gap (in seconds) that is acceptable for a turn? Have you counted it out 1000-1, 1000-2, 1000-3? Professional instructors suggest five seconds minimum, 10 seconds for beginning drivers. Do you look beyond the immediate traffic in the intersection (to the right and left) before you make a turn? Phil Berardelli in *Safe Young Drivers* [82] advocates the three second rule: after you complete your left turn, when you are completely out of traffic, it should take about three seconds for the traffic to pass in your rearview mirror. That's how you'll know you've turned with plenty of time.

Stage 2: Reinforcing Hazard Awareness

The next exercises reinforce your new visual scanning skills with on-the-road exercises.

Exercise 5. Narrative Driving

Problem:
As important as exercises one through four are in improving our chances of survival on the highway, they are not the kinds of activity that we normally engage in on the road. We take our visual attention for granted.

Solution:
Talking about how you are improving your visual attention is one way to reinforce the new eye movement patterns that you are developing. This exercise should take at least five minutes. Narrative driving is commonly used by race car drivers when they are having trouble with a particular corner; they slowly drive (or even walk) that section of the track, and identify and *talk out* specific visual reference points. This exercise is particularly useful to novice drivers and elderly drivers, but it can also give experienced drivers an opportunity to really think about what they are seeing. It is commonly used in police driver training.

Exercise:
Drive with a partner, and talk out all of the relevant information in the scene. This exercise takes about five minutes.

The most valuable part of this exercise is for the passenger to *listen* without speaking while the driver is narrating.

In the first two minutes, when it's safe to do so and you have the undivided attention of your passenger coach, describe the potential hazards that are in all parts of the scene. Don't forget to turn your head to the side, and use the rear view and side mirrors. The listener may comment at the end of two minutes on elements of the traffic scene that he or she felt were particularly important. What was relevant? What wasn't? What did he or she notice that you did not, and where was it?

It is interesting to talk out the number of signs and signals, cues and movements in the field of view while stopped at a busy intersection. Sometimes, just counting all the signs and agreeing on a tally can be a worthwhile challenge.

In the second two minutes, talk out the relevant potential hazards that are moving in all parts of the scene. How are some threats different from others? Did talking about it make you more aware of hazards? As the listener comments, did he or she notice additional potential moving hazards?

In the last minute, talk out what you anticipate as potential hazards in traffic (that you did not anticipate before the exercise). Narrative driving can be done once a week for just five minutes at a time, whenever you are driving with a passenger. It is a great no-cost way to stay alert. Professional instructors in law enforcement say *"Stay alert—stay alive."*

Caution: When a beginning teen is driving and narrating, a parent passenger's responsibility is to keep coaching attention well ahead, and behind, on the road. There are many situations and hazards that the teen is not able to anticipate until he or she is more experienced.

Exercise 6: Managing Distractions

Problem:
Distractions take our eyes and mind off the road. Most drivers are simply not aware of how often or how long they take their eyes off the road. Most experienced driving professionals know that it only takes a second or two of inattention to produce a crash.

Solution:
Interrupt distractions with life-saving glances. Research indicates that drivers can take their eyes and minds off the road for short intervals safely. This means 1-2 second glances. The risk associated with distractions increases exponentially with the amount of time that you take your eyes (and mind) off the road. A conscious effort not to take your eyes off the road for more than a second will reduce the chances of a collision. It is not realistic to expect drivers to never take their eyes off the road. It is realistic, though, to expect drivers to learn to set limits on their distraction times.

Exercise:
This exercise allows you to become more aware of the time cost of distractions. It teaches the driver to interrupt "eyes off" activities with informative glances back to the road. Follow these steps:

1. **While sitting in your driveway or in a parking lot**, engage in a distracting activity that you might normally do during

your morning commute. For instance, count the seconds it takes you to:

- look down and reach for a cup of coffee or a drink.
- reach for something on the seat next to you.

2. Again, while sitting in your driveway or in a parking lot, do the same distracting activity, but two seconds into the activity, interrupt the activity with a conscious glance to the scene through the windshield. Was it difficult? Do you feel safer? **Repeat** glancing up and around every second.

3. Practice being conscious of how long you take your eyes off the road for different activities in the vehicle. Many drivers give up fiddling with cell phones when they see how other users lag at lights, weave, and don't hold lane position.

4. Take a hint from professional driving instructors: practice doing things by feel/touch without taking your eyes off the road at all. Reach for a drink or tune the radio without looking down.

5. Constantly remind yourself to look up and look ahead.

Exercise 7. Conscious Switching

Problem:
We become lazy and transfixed on the car we're following, the yellow line, or simply the road ahead. We don't consciously switch our attention between the wide and focused views. The tendency to tunnel after long hours behind the wheel (due to boredom) is stronger than our learned habit of switching our attention to different parts of the driving task. This type of tunneling also increases with age, vehicle speed, and general monotony.[83]

Solution:
Consciously switching attention between the focused and the wide view is one way to reduce the odds that you will fall into the habit of tunnel vision. Professional drivers practice the habit of consciously moving their eyes to different views of near, far, left, and right to overcome boredom and avoid becoming hypnotized by a single "focused view."

Learning to drive safely is learning to continually move from focused to distributed attention and back, for the entire time you are on the road.

You must develop both focused and distributed attention skills. You can't learn to scan down the road and gather the whole scene while neglecting effective routines that guide focused attention close to the vehicle. Likewise, you can't exclusively focus on the lane in front of you and ignore the wide view. Learning to switch between the two processes—focused and distributed attention—enables the driver to see more effectively, with fewer and shorter fixations on relevant targets.

Exercise:

This exercise interrupts boredom and the resulting tunneling by consciously switching between the two kinds of attention: the narrow focused view and the broad view.

In the beginning, switching your attention is a conscious process that must be practiced every time you are in a car. Practice it in short bursts. Particularly at first, switching takes energy and can be overwhelming if kept up too long. The passenger who is studying each and every parked car for signs of movement will become overwhelmed with minor details, feel stressed, and may even miss important cues in other parts of the traffic scene.

At first, take just 10-15 seconds each time you are a passenger and consciously practice switching your attention from a specific object, such as the road directly ahead, to taking the wide view. Be especially attentive to movement and change. Consciously go back and forth between the two views. Repeat until you can do conscious switching for just 30 seconds without effort. How does it feel?

It is natural on long boring stretches to become "zoned out" on the road ahead. During bad weather conditions such as snow and rain, many drivers focus too closely on the vehicle to the exclusion of looking around. Conscious switching simply breaks automatic and destructive routines, whereas moving the eyes adds entertainment and diversity to the visual scene. Some drivers also report that conscious eye movements have calming and meditative effects.

Danny McKeever of Fast Lane trains drivers on the track to switch between the narrow and broad view by having a *passenger* hold a hand in front of himself or herself while riding on the track. He then instructs the student passenger to switch focus between the hand and the track beyond the hand. When the student consciously places the hand in the mental background, he or she is able to report details of the entire track. This is an exercise you can do as a passenger. You can switch attention between your hand and the roadway in milliseconds. Try it.

Stage 3: Advanced Awareness— Anticipate and Predict

In the final stages, you will use the techniques of professional drivers to lead with your eyes. You will learn to look all the way through intersections, corners, merges, and turns so that your actions become smooth and predictable to other drivers. You will learn to formulate evasive actions and ultimately become skilled at predicting the dangerous actions of others.[84]

Exercise 8. The Eyes Lead

Problem:

If you navigate turns and corners with your head and eyes straight ahead, it takes longer to react to dangers and emergencies.

Solution:

Learn to lead your steering with your eyes. Your head will follow. Train your eyes to look through the entire turn, corner or intersection. The hands follow the eyes.

Jeff Payne of Driver's Edge summarized his young drivers' skills before and after minimal track training: "The students learn to look where they want to be instead of where they are pointed." Over and over, Jeff's instructors repeat the adage that "you go where you look."

When you turn your head to where you are going, you reduce your eyes' reaction time because you decrease the amount of distance that you have to move your eyes to the next relevant cue. Even more important, by turning your head and your eyes toward the relevant target, you help to develop smooth pursuit eye-movements.

Exercise:

Learn to look all the way through corners, intersections and turns. Look well beyond where you are now to where you will be in the next 10 seconds.

Consciously practice looking through a turn *whenever you are a passenger* until it becomes a habit. As the driver enters a right turn in a city intersection, try to take a snapshot view of the corner with your head straight ahead on the old path. Can you do it? What do you see? At the next right turn, turn your head and eyes to the right and look through the whole corner. Try the snapshot view of the corner with your head turned. Take in the curb, the white crosswalk line, any bicyclists or pedestrians, the traffic on the other side of the intersection, and where the car will be in the next 10 seconds. Make a conscious effort to look well beyond the immediate intersection. Does it work?

Here's another exercise. As the driver starts a left turn into a parking lot, look left-right-left to gauge approaching traffic. (This is another way to say that you should be aware of your immediate situation before you plan your next move.) Then turn your head to the left and look through to where you will be in the next 10 seconds. After completing the turn, ask yourself if you were able to project a visual image of where the car would be and how it would go through the intersection before the driver stepped on the accelerator. Did the technique allow you to spot events on the other side of the intersection that you would not have done otherwise? Can you see

how the technique made you more aware of
bicyclists or pedestrians in the intersection?
Did the technique make you more aware of
how fast traffic was approaching the
intersection? Of other vehicles entering or
exiting the parking lot?

Exercise 9. The Visual Plan

Problem:

The odds of disorientation and
tunneling go up when the driver does not have
a thought-out plan for an evasive action or
maneuver.

Solution:

One part of learning to drive safely is to
always have a plan. In an emergency, a well-
rehearsed plan of action can reduce your
natural tendency to zoom in and narrow your
vision. A plan reduces the effects of emotional
arousal and helps maintain calm control of
attention. If you push your visual attention far
ahead and make a conscious path, the odds
are good that your hands and your vehicle will
be able to follow. Of course, practicing a plan
on a driving course will ensure that the plan
can be carried out.

*A plan reduces the element of surprise and
allows you to become visually familiar with the
possible actions that you might take in an
emergency.*

Exercise:

This exercise teaches you to formulate
a visual and mental plan for evasive actions in

case of an emergency. A visual plan is a prerequisite to a successful evasive maneuver.

We learn by doing. As we have seen in earlier chapters, the new research on visual routines suggests that we learn by moving our eyes through the scene that we are about to navigate. Moving our eyes is an essential component of the learning process. Likewise, it stands to reason that if you practice moving your eyes through an escape route while driving under calm conditions, you will be more likely to have smooth pursuit eye movements available when a crisis unfolds and the demands on your mental resources are at a maximum. In the words of Dan McKeever, if you guide your visual attention to an escape route, your hands will be able to follow. In contrast, if you have no visual plan, your hands will freeze.

Imagine that you are on a four-lane expressway (four lanes in one direction) and it is starting to get crowded. You notice that a long tractor-trailer has edged up to your right side, blocking any possible escape in that direction. Now you notice that there is a pickup truck in front of you fully loaded with furniture, some of which is clearly not tied down. The left lane has a narrow shoulder. As you check the rearview mirror, you become aware that a cluster of cars is closing the gap behind you. What can you do to give yourself some operating room in this situation? Move your eyes over the escape route. Does this open up new actions?

Even if you are driving alone, it is effective to talk out what might happen if everyone suddenly stops in front of you and the cars in your rear view mirror are approaching too fast. What can you do to escape? Run off the shoulder? Pull to the left or right? Flash your brake lights? Talk it out; there's no one right answer, it will depend on the situation. Move your eyes over the escape route. Think about the actions you will have to take to make your escape. In time, searching out potential escape routes will become a habit.

Exercise 10. Anticipate and Predict

Problem:

Becoming angry and "losing your cool" in traffic dramatically increases the odds that you will tunnel in an emergency. Anger and emotional arousal prevent you from taking the wide view and spotting new hazards. More important, anger causes you to ignore subtle cues that signal the actions of other drivers.

Solution:

Once you learn how to control your visual attention, you are more likely to stay calm and drive smoothly. You also become more aware of the dangerous actions of other drivers well before they make them. You become better at anticipating and predicting their moves.

Exercise:

This encompasses several mental exercises. The exercises emphasize using your visual attention skills to anticipate and predict the actions of other drivers so that you can stay calm and cool when new hazardous situations unfold.

- Don't let yourself be surprised. Work to anticipate and predict the moves of other drivers. Rather than get upset at the driver who is going to cut you off without signaling, see if you can detect subtle, relevant cues that allow you to predict his or her actions. You can tell 95% of the time when someone is going to cut you off. What cues are there? Are you looking at the other driver's head movements? How his or her tires are pointing? Rate of speed? There is a difference between being annoyed and surprised. If you are attentive, you will be surprised how often you are *not* surprised. You should start to realize that you are a lot smarter than the driver who is not aware. Congratulate yourself when you correctly predict another driver's hazardous move. The adage "drive defensively and watch out for the other guy" is true. The defensive driver is one who can maintain vehicle control regardless of other drivers, weather, poor roads, or unexpected hazards.

- Use turn signals. If you use your turn signals at every opportunity, you allow other drivers to anticipate and predict your intentions and your next moves. You may have it clear in your mind that you intend to turn left from a turn lane, but the driver in approaching traffic might need a signal that your car might cross the intersection. Signaling respects other drivers' disciplined attention.

- Avoid road rage. Road rage is an attitude that can cause you to become overwhelmed, both short term and long term. Police instructors teach that aggressive driving will put drivers into situations that they do not have the skills to recover from, even if they are good or above average drivers. The aggressive driver may not realize that tunnel vision happens with increased anger. Consequently, an angry driver is seldom a proficient driver.

- Calm down during rush hour. Aggressive driving increases with traffic congestion, but that's not the whole story. When congestion is coupled with a sense of urgency, as in rush hour, acts such as cutting across one or more lanes, honking, and passing on the shoulders increase even more.[85] Drivers are more likely to be aggressive when time is at a premium, not during non-rush and weekend hours. Take the time pressure off during your commute and view the interval as a psychological rest period. You will drive less aggressively, feel less anger, and be more ready for an emergency.

- When traffic seems overwhelming, practice the first four exercises to expand your effective field of view. It's amazing how congested traffic, like weather and boredom, automatically causes most drivers to tunnel. We focus on the line of traffic ahead of us, the possible source of the congestion, and the line formed between the cars in adjacent lanes ahead. Don't let the traffic pattern lock you into gazing just at one focal point; force yourself to look around. Don't hesitate to do the conscious switching exercise when you feel that you are zoning out on the traffic scene. When you are feeling bored, try deliberately moving your eyes to new targets that you may not have used before.

• Turn off cell and stereo. When traffic becomes fast-paced and congested, try turning off the stereo or cell phone and focus on how smoothly you are driving. Tune in to what is happening: the sense of movement, vehicle sounds, traffic movement, and the sound of your tires on the road.

• Be aware of muscle tension. When you start to tunnel, and you suddenly realize it, become aware of any increase in tension in your neck and back muscles. Are you gripping the steering wheel more tightly in heavy traffic? Are your wrist muscles tired when you get home? Expand your view, relax your grip, and release the tension in your back.

• Recognize your successes. Was your trip enjoyable? Did you do something on the drive home that improved your visual attention? Did you predict a poor driver's actions? Did you spot a bad pothole more quickly? Did you plan an evasive maneuver that you wouldn't have thought about before?

Stage 4: The Aware Driver

Taking Control of Visual Attention

Practice leads to automatic behaviors. As you do the exercises in this book as a passenger, you will notice that you will not have to consciously call them up each time to drive; you will start to move your eyes to relevant dangers automatically. You've started the process of developing disciplined attention, which brings other rewards.

Moving the eyes and achieving a sense of balance and control are calming. Almost all meditation and relaxation techniques train the mind to focus on simple, predictable eye movement patterns. Driving is no different. The driver who achieves control of his or her visual attention soon learns that is it one of the most relaxing activities he or she can do. If your attention is frazzled and distracted, you will also feel agitated and upset. You are clearly not in control. If your attention is disciplined, you will feel calm and in control.

Malcom Gladwell in The New Yorker lays out in detail how traffic fatality rates vary strongly with driver behavior.[86] Contrary to the prevailing wisdom, which suggests that larger vehicles and more bulk are more protective than driver skills, Gladwell argues that drivers who stay alert and take control are in reality much safer than drivers who accept the illusion that accidents are inevitable.

As we have learned, experienced drivers react faster and more efficiently in a crisis. Professionally trained drivers learn how to exert a degree of control over what might seem to many drivers to be uncontrollable events.

You can't control other drivers, but you can control your attention. When you are not paying conscious attention to the road ahead, you are more likely to be surprised by the moves of other drivers and feel frustrated and angry. When you are focused on the road and traffic and driving challenges, you will be less at the mercy of careless drivers and be in control.

Drivers who are enthusiasts and truly enjoy driving talk frequently about their ability to achieve a unique, almost transcendental focus. They find driving to be a new opportunity and each time they start the car, they are open to developing new ways to become more aware of their environment. They have discovered that driving can open the mind to new experiences.

Like enthusiasts and professionals, keep your eyes and your mind moving.

Feedback

Please give us feedback. After you do the exercises in this book, answer the again. We are interested in how the exercises influence your driving. Please log onto *www.disciplined-attention.com* and tell us how the exercises worked. Tell us how they didn't work. Do you have suggestions for other drivers on how to improve visual attention on the road?

Send your suggestions to: *www.disciplined-attention.com*

Tunneling: Can you send us examples of how you have tunneled in response to a road hazard? A road emergency? A non-driving example? Do you have new examples of target fixation while driving? In sports?

Calming: Please send us examples of how moving your eyes over a scene has helped you become calm. Was the scene real or imagined? Are there driving situations where you have used conscious eye movements to improve your performance?

Any suggestions for improving the text in this book? Any suggestions for improving the exercises?

Thanks for taking the *Disciplined Attention* journey and becoming a safer, better driver.

References

[1] Williams, A.F., Paek, N.N., & Lund, A.K. (1995). Factors that drivers say motivate safe driving practices. *Journal of Safety Research, 26* (2), 119–124.

[2] Csikszentmihalyi, M. (1990). *Flow: the psychology of optimal experience.* New York: Harper & Row.

[3] Berardelli, P. (2000). *Safe young drivers: a guide for parents and teens.* Vienna, VA: Nautilus Communications, Inc.

[4] Easterbrook, J.A. (1959). The effect of emotion on cue utilization and the organization of behavior. *Psychological Review, 66* (3), 183–201.

[5] Christianson, S. (1992). Emotional stress and eyewitness memory: a critical review. *Psychological Bulletin, 112,* 284–309.

[6] Ball, K., & Owsley, C. (1993). The useful field of view test: a new technique for evaluating age-related declines in visual function. *Journal of the American Optometric Association, 64,* 71–79.

[7] Ball, K., Beard, B., Roenker, D., Miller, R., & Griggs, D. (1988). Age and visual search: expanding the useful field of view. *Journal of the Optical Society of America, 5,* 2210–2219.

[8] AAA Foundation for Traffic Safety, (2004). *Pay Attention!, Stock 962.* Washington D.C. Retrieved from *http://www.aaafoundation.org/pdf/DistractedDrivingBrochure.pdf.*

9 Pelz, J.B., Canosa, R.L., Kucharczyk, D., Babcock, J., Silver, A., & Konno, D. (2000). Portable eyetracking: a study of natural eye movements. *Human Vision and Electronic Imaging V.* In B.E. Rogowitz and T.N. Pappas (Eds.) *SPIE Proceedings 3959,* (pp. 566–582).

10 Ullman, S. (1984). Visual routines. *Cognition, 18,* 97-159.

11 Hayhoe, M. (2000). Vision using routines: a functional account of vision. *Visual Cognition, 7* (1/2/3), 43-64.

12 Cavanagh, P., Labianca, A.T., & Thornton, I.M. (2001). Attention-based visual routines: sprites. *Cognition, 80,* 47-60.

13 Land, M.F. (1998). The visual control of steering. In L.R. Harris & M. Jenkin (Eds.) *Vision and Action,* 163–180. Cambridge University Press.

14 Land, M.F. & Lee, D.N. (1994). Where we look when we steer. *Nature, 369,* 742–744.

15 Land, M.F. & Horwood, J. (1995). Which parts of the road guide steering. *Nature, 377,* 339–340.

16 Association of professional Law enforcement Emergency vehicle Response Trainers (http://*www.alertinternational.com*)

17 McKeever, Dan, chief driving instructor for ALEM International (http://*www.aleminternational.com*).

18 Chen, L., Baker, S.P., Braver, E.R., & Li, G. (2000). Carrying passengers as a risk factor for crashes fatal to 16- and 17-year-old

drivers. *The Journal of the American Medical Association, 283* (12), 1578–1582.

[19] National Institute on Alcohol Abuse and Alcoholism, (1994). *Alcohol-Related Impairment, Alcohol Alert, No. 25 PH 351.* Retrieved from *http://www.niaaa.nih.gov/publications/aa 25.htm.*

[20] Katoh, Z. (1988). Slowing effects of alcohol on voluntary eye movements. *Aviation, Space, and Environmental Medicine 59,* 606–610.

[21] Mills, K.C., Parkman, K. M. & Spruill, S.E. (1996). A PC-based software test for measuring alcohol and drug effects in human subjects. *Alcoholism: Clinical and Experimental Research, 20* (9), 1582–1591.

[22] Strayer, D.L., Drews, F.A., & Crouch, D.J. (2002). Fatal distraction? A comparison of the cell-phone driver and the drunk driver. *Driver Assessment, 2002.* Park City, Utah.

[23] Williams, A.F. (2003). Views of U.S. drivers about driving safety. *Journal of Safety Research, 34* (5), 491–504.

[24] Noise is used here in the context of signal detection theory in which there are two discrete states of the world, *signals* to be attended to and *noise* that distracts or disrupts attention.

[25] Green, D.M., & Swets, J.A. (1966). Signal detection theory and psychophysics. New York: Wiley.

[26] Ramaekers, J.G., Berghaus, G., van Laar, M., & Drummer, O.H. (2004). Dose related risk of

motor vehicle crashes after cannabis use. *Drug and Alcohol Dependence, 73,* 109–119.

[27] Eby, D.W., Molnar, L.J., Shope, J.T., Vivoda, J.M., & Fordyce, T.A. (2003). Improving older driver knowledge and self-awareness through self-assessment: the driving decisions workbook. *Journal of Safety Research, 34,* 371–381.

[28] Green, C.S. & Bavelier, D. (2003). Action video game modifies visual selective attention. *Nature, 423,* 534–537.

[29] Quality Planning Corporation, San Francisco, Oct 20, 2003 press release.

[30] Dennis, M. (2003). Is it an accident or is it a crash? *The Chronicle of the American Driver and Traffic Safety Education Association, 51* (4), 4.

[31] Williams, A.F. (2003). Views of U.S. drivers about driving safety. *Journal of Safety Research, 34* (5), 491-504.

[32] LeDoux, Joseph (1996). *The emotional brain.* New York: Touchstone.

[33] Johnson, Steven (2004). *Mind wide open, your brain and the neuroscience of everyday life.* New York: Scribner.

[34] Pannasch, S., Dornhoefer, S.M., Unema, P.J.A., & Velichkovsky, B.M. (2001). The omnipresent prolongation of visual fixations: saccades are inhibited by changes in situation and in subject's activity. *Vision Research, 41,* 3345–3351.

[35] John Lenneman is a researcher at General Motors who has conducted initial studies of

how our nervous system functions when we drive. According to John and his colleague Richard Backs at Central Michigan University, the two components of the driver's autonomic nervous system couple and uncouple in dance-like patterns that depend on mental workload and visual demand. However, the relationship between mental workload and heart rate is not as straightforward as once assumed and current research is finding that no single measure can account for driver mental workload. The heart is innervated by both the sympathetic and parasympathetic branches of the autonomic nervous system (ANS) that have unique effects on heart rate, depending on the circumstances. Generally, heart rate will increase with "cognitive or perceptual workload," but not always. While driving performance decreases with measures of visual demand, changes in heart rate may sometimes slow when visual demand increases. The extent of sympathetic and parasympathetic "coupling" may depend on the perceived workload. See:

Backs, R.W., Lenneman, J.K., Wetzel, J.M., & Green, P. (in press) Cardiac measures of driver workload during simulated driving with and without visual occlusion. *Human Factors.*

Lenneman, J.K. & Backs, R.W. (2003). The evolution of autonomic space as a method of mental workload assessment while driving. *Driver Assessment 2003,* Park City, Utah.

Backs, R. (2001). An automatic space approach to the psychophysiological assessment of mental workload. In

P.A. Hancock, & P.A. Desmond
(Eds.), *Stress, Workload, and Fatigue*
(pp. 279–289). Lawrence Erlbaum
and Associates: Mahwah, NJ.

[36] Carrasco, M., McElree, B., Denisova, K. &
Giordano, A.M. (2003). Speed of visual
processing increases with eccentricity.
Nature Neuroscience, 6 (7) 699–670.

[37] For a discussion of the "what and now" visual
systems see O'Regan, J.K. & Noë, A. (2001).
A Sensormotor account of vision and visual
consciousness. *Behavioral and Brain
Sciences, 24,* 939–1031.

[38] Sacks, Oliver (2004, August 23). Speed:
aberrations of time and movement. *The
New Yorker,* pp. 60-69.

[39] Livingstone, M.S., & Hubel, D. (1988).
Segregation of form, color, movement, and
depth: anatomy, physiology, and
perception. *Science, 240* (4853), 740–749.

[40] Pannasch, S., Dornhoefer, S.M., Unema, P.J.A.,
& Velichkovsky, B.M. (2001). The
omnipresent prolongation of visual
fixations: saccades are inhibited by changes
in situation and in subject's activity. *Vision
Research, 41,* 3345–3351.

[41] Sokolov, E.N. & Vinogradova, O. (1975).
Neuronal mechanisms of the orienting reflex.
Lawrence Erlbaum Associates: Hillsdale,
NJ.

[42] Muttart, J.W. (2003). Development and
evaluation of driver response time
. predictors based upon meta analysis. *SAE
Technical Paper Series (SP-1773) SAE World*

Congress, Detroit, Michigan, retrieved from http://*www.sae.org.*

[43] Simons, D.J. & Chabris, C.F. (1999). Gorillas in our midst: sustained inattentional blindness for dynamic events. *Perception, 28,* 1059–1074.

[44] Strayer, D., Drews, F.A., & Johnston, W.A. (2003). Inattention blindness behind the wheel: cell phone induced failures of visual attention during simulated driving. *Journal of Experimental Psychology: Applied, 9* (1), 23–32.

[45] Horswill, M.S. & McKenna, F.P. (in press) Drivers' hazard perception ability: situation awareness on the road.

[46] Horswill, M. (2001). Public lecture, February 27, 2001, University of Reading, UK. Retrieved from *http://www.personal.rdg.ac.uk/~sxrhorsl/*

[47] Horswill, M.S. & Helman, S. (2003). A behavioral comparison between motorcyclists and a matched group of non-motorcycling car drivers: factors influencing accident risk. *Accident Analysis & Prevention, 35* (4), 589–597.

[48] Horswill, M.S. & McKenna, F.P. (1999). The development, validation, and application of a video-based technique for measuring risk taking behavior: drivers' speed choice. *Journal of Applied Psychology, 84* (6) 977–985.

[49] "The National Conference of State Legislatures (NCSL) has developed a database for state legislation concerning driver distractions and technology in motor vehicles. The

database is intended to capture state legislative efforts to address driver distraction issues including proposed restrictions on wireless or cellular telephones. The database includes brief summaries of the legislation, bill status information, the bill sponsor, and links to the legislation. Users can search the database by year, state, bill status, and legislation scope. As with all legislation, the database is a work in progress. Generally, legislation information is updated on a weekly basis." National Conference of State Legislatures, retrieved from *http://www.ncsl.org/programs/transportati on/DRFOCUS.htm*

[50] Stutts, J., Feaganes, J., Rodgman, E., Hamlett, C., Meadows, T., Reinfurt, D., Gish, K., Mercadante, M. & Staplin, L., (2003). *Distractions in everyday driving,* from AAA Foundation for Traffic Safety, from *http://www.aaafoundation.org*

[51] Cooper, P.J. & Zheng, Y. (2002). Turning gap acceptance decision making: the impact of driver distraction. *Journal of Safety Research, 33* (3) 321–335.

[52] Cooper, P.J., Zheng, Y., Richard, C., Vavrik, J., Heinrichs, B., & Siegmund, G. (2003). The impact of hands-free message reception/response on driving task performance. *Accident Analysis & Prevention, 35,* 23–3.

[53] Patten, C.J., Kircher, A., Ostlund, J., & Nilsson, L. (2004). Using mobile telephones: cognitive workload and attention resource allocation. *Accident Analysis & Prevention, 36* (3), 341–350.

[54] Hancock, P.A., Lesch, M., & Simmons, L. (2003). The distraction effects of phone use during a crucial driving maneuver. *Accident Analysis & Prevention, 35* (4), 501–514.

[55] Horswill, M.S. & McKenna, F.P. (1999). The effect of interference on dynamic risk-taking judgments. *British Journal of Psychology, 90,* 189–199.

[56] *(http://www.mason-dixon.com) (http://www.safetydrivingtest.com) (http://www.trafficsafety.net)*

[57] Miller, M.J. & Smith, R.A. (2003). The relationship of credit-based insurance scores to private passenger automobile insurance loss propensity. EPIC Actuaries, LLC, P.O. Box 628, Minocqua, WI 54548, retrieved from *http://www.epicactuaries.com/Publications. asp*

[58] Legarde, E., Chastang, J.F., Gueguen, A., Coeuret-Pellicer, M., Chiron, M. & Lafont, S. (2004) Emotional stress and traffic accidents: The impact of separation and divorce. *Epidemiology,* 15(6), 762-766.

[59] Wickens, C.D. & Hollands, J.G. (2000). *Engineering Psychology and Human Performance (Third Edition).* Upper Saddle River, New Jersey: Prentice Hall.

[60] Just over 2% of the cadets are women.

[61] In one of our studies, we sampled heart rates from the cadets as they progressed through training. We had a chance to sample heart rates in the lab before and after stressful simulations, on the track for the first time, and in some cases during the first drive in a

car. In the lab, the baseline or resting heart rates averaged 50 to 70 beats per minute. During mildly stressful computerized testing, heart rates increased about 10%. Then we moved to the track. Heart rates for the cadets jumped to 90 to 115 beats per minute before the track testing. These are heart rates while standing in the pit. When the track experience began, we observed heart rates of 140 to160 beats per minute.

[62] Paul Whitsell is the assistant executive director of PPCT Management Systems, Inc., which is the largest defensive tactics training organization in the world (*www.ppct.com*).

[63] Mills, K.C., Parkman, K. M., & Spruill, S.E. (1996). A PC-based software test for measuring alcohol and drug effects in human subjects. *Alcoholism: Clinical and Experimental Research, 20* (9), 1582–1591.

[64] Mills, K.C., Parkman, K.M., Smith, G.A., & Rosendahl, F. (1999). Prediction of driving performance through computerized testing: high-risk driver assessment and training. *Transportation Research Record, 1689,* 18–24.

[65] Chen, L., Baker, S.P., Braver, E.R., & Li, G. (2000). Carrying passengers as a risk factor for crashes fatal to 16- and 17-year-old drivers. *The Journal of the American Medical Association, 283* (12), 1578–1582.

[66] Berardelli, P. (2000). *Safe young drivers: a guide for parents and teens.* Vienna, VA: Nautilus Communications, Inc.

[67] Mourant, R.R. & Rockwell, T.H. (1972). Strategies of visual search by novice and

experienced drivers. *Human Factors, 14* (4), 325–335.

[68] Hughes, C.J., personal communication, (C.J. Hughes, University of Sussex, Brighton, East Sussex, UK) Feb 15, 2003.

[69] Crundall, D.E., Underwood, G., & Chapman, P. (1999). Driving experience and the functional field of view. *Perception, 28* (9), 1075–1087.

[70] Underwood, G., Crundall, D., & Chapman, P. (2002). Selective attention while driving: the role of experience in hazard detection and general surveillance. *Ergonomics, 45* (1), 1–12.

[71] Chapman, P.R. & Underwood, G. (1998). Visual search of driving situations: danger and experience. *Perception, 27* (8), 951–964.

[72] Underwood, G., Chapman, P., Berger, Z., & Crundall (2003). Driving experience, attentional focusing, and the recall of recently inspected events. *Transportation Research Part F 6,* 289–304.

[73] Allison, George, personal communication, (George Allison, Program Specialist, Driver Training Department of Homeland Security (DHS), Federal Law Enforcement Training Center (FLETC)) Cheltenham, MD 20623–5000, May 15, 2004.

[74] Horswill, M.S. & McKenna, F.P. (in press) Drivers' hazard perception ability: situation awareness on the road.

[75] Owsley, C., Ball, K., McGwin, G., Sloane, M., Roenker, D., White, M., & Overley, T. (1998). Visual processing impairment and

risk of motor vehicle crash among older adults. *Journal of the American Medical Association, 279,* 1083-1088.

[76] Ball, K. & Owsley, C. (1993). The useful field of view test: a new technique for evaluating age-related declines in visual function. *Journal of the American Optometric Association, 64,* 71-79.

[77] Roenker, D.L., Cissell, G.M., Ball, K., Wadley, V., & Edwards, J. (2003). Speed of processing and driving simulator training result in improved driving performance. *Human Factors, 45* (2), 218-233.

[78] Green, C.S. & Bavelier, D. (2003). Action video game modifies visual selective attention. *Nature, 423,* 534-537.

[79] Fisher, D.L., Laurie, N.E., Glaser, R., Connerney, K., Pollatsek, A., Duffy, S.A., & Brock, J. (2002). Use of fixed based driving simulator to evaluate the effects of experience and PC-based risk awareness training on drivers' decisions. *Human Factors, 44* (2), 287-302.

[80] AAA Foundation for Traffic Safety, *Drivers ZED (Zero Errors Driving)©,* from *http://www.aaafoundation.org*

[81] Chapman, P., Underwood, G., & Roberts, K. (2002). Visual search patterns in trained and untrained novice drivers. *Transportation Research Part F 5,* 157-167.

[82] Berardelli, P. (2000). *Safe young drivers: a guide for parents and teens.* Vienna, VA: Nautilus Communications, Inc.

[83] Roge, J., Pebayle, T., Lambillotte, E., Spitzenstetter, F., Giselbrecht, D., & Muzet,

A. (2004). Influence of age, speed and duration of monotonous driving task in traffic on the driver's useful visual field. *Vision Research, 44* (23), 2737-2744.

[84] Schaffer, Paul, Master Law Enforcement Program Specialist in driver training at the Federal Law Enforcement Training Center in Glynco, Georgia, offers a discussion of how to "Read the Road" for different types of corners on his web site: *www.ledtrs.com/content/publication_links.htm*

[85] Shinar, D. & Compton, R. (2004). Aggressive driving: an observational study of driver, vehicle, and situational variables. *Accident Analysis & Prevention, 36* (3), 429-437.

[86] Gladwell, M. (2004, January 12). Big and bad: how the S.U.V. ran over automotive safety. *The New Yorker*, pp. 28-33.

Index

Notes

Notes

Notes

Profile Press
Order Form

Sold to:

Name: _____

Company: _____

Street Address: _____

City: _____

State: _____ Zip: _____

Email: _____

Telephone:_____

☐ Yes, I would like to order _____ copies of *"Disciplined Attention"* for $29.95 a copy. (please inquire about bulk order prices.)

☐ Yes, I would like Kenneth C. Mills to conduct a Disciplined Attention workshop at our company, association, school, or organization. Please call me.

Shipping/handling fees apply. North Carolina residents must add appropriate tax (7 or 7.5%).

Please mail or fax order form to:
Profile Press
111 Cloister Court Suite 212
Chapel Hill, NC 27514
Fax: 919.408.0643 Phone: 919.408.0745

Order online ***www.disciplined-attention.com.***

We accept MasterCard, Visa, Company Check or Purchase Order. Please call in credit card orders.